HOW TO FIND
TREASURE
FROM SPACE

THE EXPERT GUIDE TO
METEORITE HUNTING
AND IDENTIFICATION

GEOFFREY NOTKIN

Introduction by **Christopher Cokinos**, author of
The Fallen Sky: An Intimate History of Shooting Stars

Edited by Nancy and Dr. Larry Lebofsky
Managing Editor, Melissa Silva

STANEGATE PRESS

Photography

Qynne Arnold
Steve Arnold
Abdellah Azizi
Sonya Gay Bourn
Leigh Anne DelRay Crowell
John Kashuba
Robert Matson
Christian B. Meza
Lisa Marie Morrison
Suzanne Morrison
NASA/JPL/USGS
Geoffrey Notkin
Caroline Palmer

Illustrations

Antonia Andros
Timothy Arbon

Prop Artist

Jessica Milligan Stone

Some material in this book originally appeared in a different
form in the author's science column *Meteorwritings* for Geology.com.
That material is reproduced here with the gracious permission
of publisher Dr. Hobart King.

Design and art direction by Stanegate Studios
Published by Stanegate Press, Inc.
www.stanegatepress.com

Revised and expanded third edition
ISBN 978-0-9847548-8-5

Printed in the United States of America
© 2012–2019 by Stanegate Press, Inc., except where noted

For Allan Lang,
friend, colleague, mentor,
and a giant in both meteoritics
and paleontology.

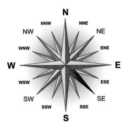

PREFACE

Meteorites are the most remarkable things on our planet, and they are not even from this planet. They are pieces of extraterrestrial rock and metal that have fallen onto the surface of our planet, Earth. Meteorites are a tangible link with an existence outside of the world we know and are, literally, visitors from outer space. They are important to researchers because within them are clues to the origin of suns, planets, asteroids and, possibly, even life itself. They are valued by enthusiasts because a space rock is, perhaps, the most intriguing of all collectibles. The rarity of meteorites and the fact that they are the only way in which most of us will ever be able to touch a piece of an alien world makes them of great interest to an ever-expanding network of devotees. Collecting and hunting for meteorites are exciting hobbies that are rapidly growing in popularity.

Meteorites first appeared in my life when I was about six years old. I grew up in Greater London and was an avid rock hound from an early age. My parents encouraged my interest in science: my father sharing his love of astronomy and telescopes, and my mother accompanying me on frequent trips to science museums and on fossil hunting missions into the chalk quarries of southern England.

It all came together for me when, as a little boy, I first walked into the Hall of Meteorites in London's Geological Museum. In a moment of revelation, I realized that by recovering and studying meteorites, we were looking deep into the history, mystery, and makeup of other worlds. For me, meteorites became the locus where astronomy and geology became one. That flash of insight was the spark that ignited a lifelong passion for space rocks.

I found my first meteorite in 1994. Three years later I met Steve Arnold, an experienced meteorite hunter, and joined him on a sometimes grueling, sometimes thrilling expedition to the Atacama Desert in Chile on the hunt for space rocks. My life would never be the same.

Steve and I became friends, expedition partners, and—many years later—hosts of the Science Channel's multi-award-winning adventure television series *Meteorite Men,* which has aired all over the world and has been seen by tens of millions of people.

In my career I have found literally thousands of space rocks. Some were deeply buried and had been hidden underground for many centuries. Others were lying right on the surface when I spotted them, only two or three days after falling from the sky. The smallest meteorite I ever recovered weighed only 0.2 grams—or 1/140th of an ounce—and the largest was a staggering 124 kg (273 lbs).

If you are to be successful, as I have been, at tracking and recovering that most precious and desirable of quarries, you need to very clearly understand what you are hunting for; you have to understand what meteorites are, where they come from, and what they look like. I have, therefore, devoted the first part of the book to discussing meteorite types, origins, and characteristics, with the assumption that you cannot find something if you do not first know what it looks like. To that end, I have collected the very best meteorite photographs I could. Some were taken by me or my colleagues in the field at the very moment of discovery! Some of the space rocks pictured in this work are in my personal collection; others are in the permanent reference collection of my company, Aerolite Meteorites, Incorporated.

In certain photographs, you will notice a black cube placed next to the subject meteorite. This is an aluminum scale cube, 1 cm along each face. Scale cubes are used in scientific photography to provide a visible frame of reference for gauging the size of the specimen.

If the idea of exploring strange landscapes in the hope of discovering ancient visitors from space lights a spark inside you, then you are the person for whom I wrote this book. My journey has been long and fascinating and, after hundreds of emails and phone calls from people who wanted to know more about space rocks and how to find them, I came to the realization that there was a void within the world of meteorites. Many people want to go on an adventure and find their own space rock, but there has never been a guide book to help them along the way—until now. In *How to Find Treasure from Space: The Expert Guide to Meteorite Hunting and Identification* I share my personal knowledge and experience—gathered the hard way over scores of expeditions, hundreds of thousands of miles, many countries and many years—with those who dream of finding their own meteorites.

After all, what could be more exciting and amazing than looking for lost pieces of the universe that have fallen to Earth?

Geoffrey Notkin

TABLE OF CONTENTS

INTRODUCTION

What's the most interesting thing within 50 or 60 miles of your house?

A strip mall?

An art museum?

A national park?

What about outer space?

Sure, outer space—if your Buick could achieve escape velocity. Think of it. Space is that close and that far away. After all, your Buick can't fly at Mach 34, and only about 500 people have ever flown in space.

So if you're interested in the cosmos, you have to be content with NASA TV, *2001* reruns and summer stargazing, right?

Not if you become a collector of rocks from space. Or, better yet, a person who actually hunts for space rocks; who scours deserts and parking lots, farms and mountainsides for meteorites, those primordial bits of the asteroid belt, the Moon or Mars that are just waiting to be discovered.

Meteorites are often called "the poor man's space probe" precisely because we don't have to go to them. They come to us. In fact, on every square mile of the planet about eight new meteorites of a gram or more will fall. A gram is pretty light, but there are enough new falls and old finds of heftier meteorites to sustain the passion of meteorite hunters like Geoffrey Notkin. And perhaps, after reading his book, meteorite hunters like you.

Meteorite hunting is a pursuit rich in connections to the stars and adventures for one's life. I wrote in my memoir and history of meteorite hunting, *The Fallen Sky*, that "the untrained eye can ... mistake some meteorites for chunks of concrete, as if a cosmic road crew had jackhammered a solar highway and sent its congeries spilling down, briefly lit, to land among soybeans or ferns. Those who quest for meteorites, however, recognize them amidst the average rubble of the earth the way a birder hears rare song untangling itself from a forest full of sound. Passion does that: It sharpens one's senses, it changes the world."

Of course it takes more than passion to be good at something. It takes knowledge. Then it takes experience. To be good at meteorite hunting, you first need this book. Here you'll learn about everything from how to identify meteorites in the field to the legalities of hunting meteorites on public and private property. You'll learn about metal detectors, fireball chases and the best places to hunt for space rocks. These and other points of information are important — crucial, in fact — but like any good teacher, Geoffrey Notkin not only gives you the details, he does so after enticing you with the big picture: "What could be more exciting and amazing," he asks, "than looking for lost pieces of the universe that have fallen to earth?" The answer: not much.

Geoffrey should know. He has revitalized and revolutionized meteorite hunting through his enthusiastic use of social media, the web and, most importantly, co-hosting the entertaining and educational television show, *Meteorite Men*. He's the perfect guide to the novice and veteran meteorite hunter. You'll find that out in this excellent book.

So save the Buick for road trips to strewnfields. Don't know what those are? Read on.

Christopher Cokinos
Author, *The Fallen Sky: An Intimate History of Shooting Stars*
Tucson, Arizona

[above] Historic example of the Brenham pallasite found by meteorite pioneer and founder of the American Meteorite Laboratory and Meteoritical Society, H.H. Nininger, in the 1930s. Note the hand-painted collection number which identifies it as originating in his collection. [right] The author on an expedition deep in the Sahara Desert. The old, dry, arid surface is an ideal environment in which to search for meteorites.

WHAT ARE METEORITES
AND WHERE DO THEY COME FROM?

Most meteorites were once part of large asteroids that broke up, or perhaps never fully formed, more than four billion years ago. A very few are known to have originated on Mars and our own Moon. These fragments of alien worlds wandered in the cold void of space for long periods of time, possibly millions of years, before crossing paths with our planet. Their tremendous velocity in space can result in an encounter with the air above us at a staggering 25,000 miles per hour or more, resulting in a short and fiery journey through our atmosphere.

Meteor is the scientific name for the atmospheric effect caused by a piece of extraterrestrial matter burning in our atmosphere, and should not be confused with the word meteorite, which refers to any material that actually lands. Meteors are bright, typically very short-lived, and caused by atmospheric drag, friction, and air compression acting on an incoming body. That body (a *meteoroid*) becomes so hot it incandesces, as does the air around it. Most meteors glow for only a few seconds or less, and that brief period of intense heat is part of what makes any surviving meteorites so very unique and fascinating. Extremely high temperatures cause surfaces to melt and flow, creating remarkable features that are entirely unique to meteorites such as *regmaglypts*, *fusion crust*, *orientation*, and *rollover lips* (see Chapter 2).

METEORS vs. METEORITES

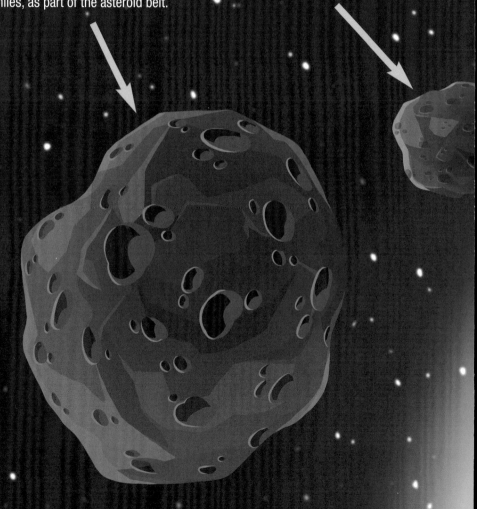

ASTEROID
Most meteorites originated on asteroids. A few come to us from Mars and our own moon. Most asteroids orbit our sun, between Mars and Jupiter, at an average distance from Earth of about 250,000,000 miles, as part of the asteroid belt.

METEOROID
A meteoroid is a potential meteorite — a physical fragment of an asteroid, planet, or moon that encounters Earth's atmosphere.

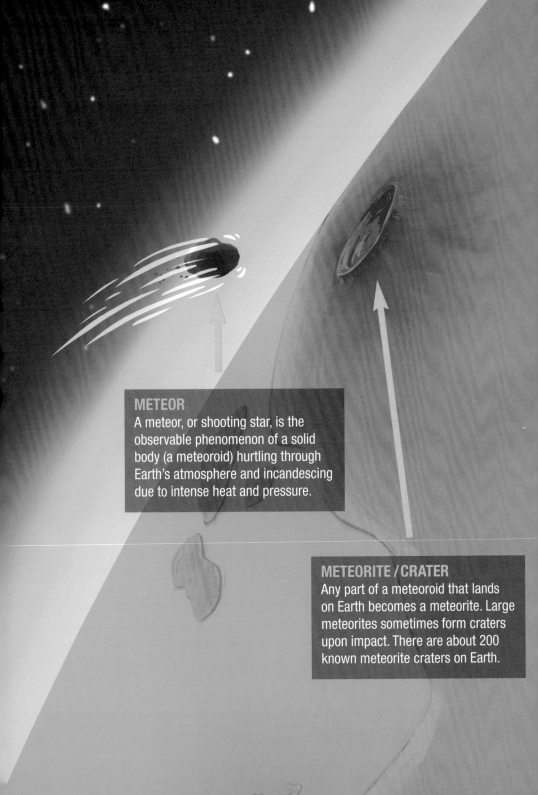

METEOR
A meteor, or shooting star, is the observable phenomenon of a solid body (a meteoroid) hurtling through Earth's atmosphere and incandescing due to intense heat and pressure.

METEORITE / CRATER
Any part of a meteoroid that lands on Earth becomes a meteorite. Large meteorites sometimes form craters upon impact. There are about 200 known meteorite craters on Earth.

[above] Artist's impression of cometary fragments on course for impact on a planet. [lower right] Grooves and craters photographed on Vesta by NASA's Dawn mission were the result of massive impacts at the asteroid's south pole and may have produced fragments that eventually landed on Earth as meteorites.

METEOR SHOWERS

There are a number of periodic meteor showers every year; the Perseids in August and the Leonids in November usually being the most interesting to observe. Annual meteor showers are the result of our planet passing through debris trails left by comets. The meteors we see during those annual displays are caused by small pieces of ice that rapidly burn up in the atmosphere and never make it to the surface of our planet. Every year, without fail, Aerolite Meteorites receives calls or emails from people who saw the Perseid meteor shower in August and believe that, as a result, meteorites fell in their yard or driveway. There has never been a documented case of a recovered meteorite being associated with one of the annual meteor showers. I know it may seem as if one landed "just over there," but the bright and brief trails you see in the night sky are the last moments of tiny fragments of cometary debris. Don't spend valuable hunting time looking for them; you will not find them.

METEOROIDS AND METEORITES

We use the term *meteoroid* to describe a potential meteorite. It is the physical body that travels through space, encounters our atmosphere and creates the phenomenon known as a meteor. To clarify: A body traveling in space towards our planet or entering our atmosphere is a meteoroid; the visual effect of superheated gas glowing around a meteoroid is described as a meteor; and anything that survives and lands on our planet's surface is a meteorite.

Meteorites are among the rarest materials found on earth. Some of them pre-date the solar system, which makes them the oldest things any human has ever touched. In order to find meteorites, it is first important to understand what they are made of and how they differ from terrestrial rocks.

ASTEROIDS: FUTURE RESOURCES FROM SPACE

Asteroids are the most abundant rocky bodies of any significant size in our solar system. They far outnumber our single sun, eight planets, and the more than 350 known moons. Most meteorites recovered on Earth were once part of asteroids, so it is accurate to describe them as asteroidal debris. Sometimes, you will hear a paleontologist or climatologist say it was an asteroid that killed the dinosaurs. While that theory is widely accepted, it can also seem misleading to some, because an asteroid — albeit a smaller one, or a fragment — also formed the famous Meteor Crater in Arizona and generated the spectacular fireball seen over the Russian city of Chelyabinsk in 2013.

Most asteroids lie in the asteroid belt between Mars and Jupiter and orbit the Sun, much as we do. It is estimated that there are between 1.1 and 1.9 million asteroids in our solar system. About 10,000 of them are described as near-Earth asteroids (NEAs) and — according to NASA — about 1,400 of those are potentially hazardous, meaning there is a chance they could crash into our planet at some point in the future. While that might be good news for meteorite collectors, it could be catastrophic for civilization.

Studying meteorites helps us understand asteroids, which is why I was invited to join Deep Space Industries, the asteroid-mining company. Meteorites have been shown to contain iron, nickel, small amounts of gold and other metals, and even carbon, water, and salt. If we can tell which asteroids produce which types of meteorites, we should be able to harvest those materials through near-future asteroid mining. Extracting resources from asteroids is a critical step in the long-term exploration and development of space. This is one way in which the study of meteorites will directly and positively affect the future of humanity.

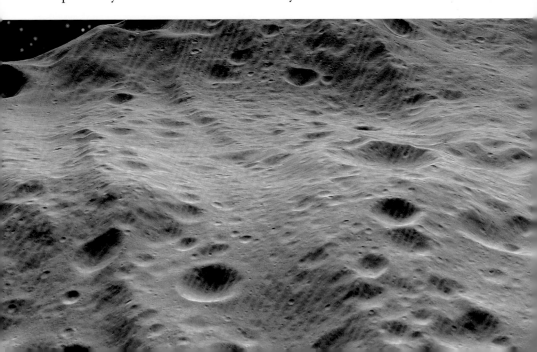

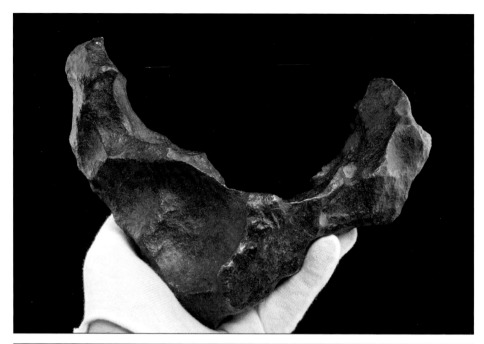

[top] Some iron meteorites, such as this Gibeon from Namibia, acquire fantastic shapes from ablation in flight, or weathering on Earth. [above] I found this Muonionalusta meteorite on an expedition to the Arctic Circle. It weighs 10 kg (22 lbs) and was photographed immediately after it came out of the ground. Note the unusual colors caused by oxidation. The mass was rounded by tumbling in an ancient glacier.

THE THREE MAIN TYPES OF METEORITES

Although there are a large number of subclasses, meteorites are divided into three main groups: irons, stones and stony-irons. Almost all meteorites contain extraterrestrial nickel and iron, and those that contain no iron at all are extremely rare.

When most people imagine what a space rock looks like, they may think of an iron meteorite and it is easy to see why. Irons are dense, very heavy for their size, and have often been forged into unusual and sometimes spectacular shapes as they plummet, melting, through our atmosphere. Although irons may be synonymous with most people's perception of a typical space rock's appearance, they are only one of three main meteorite types. Irons are rather uncommon compared to stone meteorites, especially the most abundant stone meteorite group—the ordinary chondrites.

IRON METEORITES

When I lecture on meteorites at museums, universities, spaceflight events, and schools, I love to pass around a softball-sized iron meteorite. Most people have never held a space rock in their hands and, when they do pick up an iron meteorite for the first time, their faces often light up and they exclaim: "It's so heavy!" Iron meteorites are thought to have once been part of the molten cores of long-vanished asteroids. They are among the densest materials on earth and feel heavier than terrestrial rocks of a similar size — if you have ever hefted a cannon ball or an iron dumbbell, you will get the idea.

Iron meteorites typically contain over 90% iron, along with nickel and trace elements. Even though all irons are somewhat similar in composition, they can look remarkably different on the outside, as their shapes may have been altered during flight by ablation or fragmentation or, on Earth, by weathering. Iron meteorites will attract *very* strongly to a good magnet.

[left] Iron meteorites adhere so strongly to a powerful magnet that it can take some effort to separate them! We use this fact for both meteorite identification and recovery in the field. Irons that have been on Earth for many years often oxidize to a color that is essentially identical to the sand or soil in which they are buried. When excavating a suspected iron meteorite, there are many times when my magnet found it before my eyes did. Pictured is a IIIAB iron found near the Whitecourt Crater, Alberta, Canada.

THE THREE MAIN TYPES OF METEORITES
[left to right]

IRON
Sikhote-Alin (IIAB), complete specimen with regmaglypts
Fell, eastern Siberia, February 12, 1947

STONY-IRON
Brahin (pallasite), full olivine-rich slice, as prepared in the lab
Found, Belarus, 1810

STONE
Northwest Africa (NWA) 7998, L5 chondrite, complete specimen with fusion crust and regmaglyp
Found, Morocco, 2013

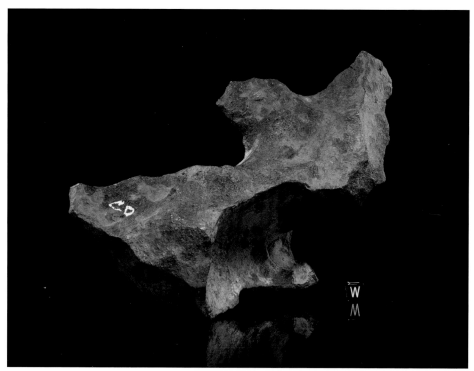

[top] Canyon Diablo iron from Meteor Crater (Barringer Crater), Arizona, with scale cube for size, uncleaned and as-found, showing natural bronze/brown patina, typical of desert irons. [above] A large Campo del Cielo iron meteorite recovered in Argentina. Note the abundant regmaglypts.

[top] 870-gram Mundrabilla iron exactly as I found it in Western Australia. Exposure to the elements for many thousands of years has caused the iron to acquire an attractive patina. [above] Iron meteorite fragment found at the Whitecourt Crater in Canada, oxidized after hundreds of years in damp ground.

STONE METEORITES

The largest group of meteorites is the stones. The majority of stone meteorites are believed to have once formed part of the outer crust of a planet or asteroid. Many stone meteorites—particularly those that have been on the surface of our planet for an extended period of time—frequently look much like terrestrial rocks, and it can take a skilled eye to spot them when meteorite hunting in the field. Freshly-fallen stones will exhibit a black fusion crust, created as the surface is heated during flight. The vast majority of stone meteorites contain enough iron for them to easily adhere to a powerful magnet.

[below] An oriented (see page 35) 21.5-gram Buzzard Coulee H4 stone meteorite, untouched by human hands and displaying excellent brown and black fusion crust, sitting where it fell among canola stalks in rural Saskatchewan. Note the rollover lip, fusion crust, and flow lines clearly visible on the surface. These are all indicators for meteorites. [below right] This fusion-crusted, oriented stone meteorite (chondrite) was found while hunting the San Juan strewnfield in Chile. The original mass weighed 870 grams. After removing some material for classification, 639.4 grams remained. Most meteorites are chondrites and most have been on the Earth for a long time. As their fusion crust oxidizes, they acquire this type of dark, black-bronze coloration. Familiarize yourself with its shape and color. This is a *very good* example of what many meteorites look like in the field.

Stone Meteorites: Ordinary Chondrites

The *chondrites* are the most abundant group of meteorites. They take their name from the *chondrules* of which they are comprised — small, colorful, grain-like inclusions which originated in the solar nebula. Chondrules pre-date the formation of our planet and the rest of the solar system, making them some of the oldest known matter available for scientific study. The presence of chondrules is a key factor in identifying many stone meteorites (see Chapter 2). Iron content is then used to differentiate the three types of ordinary chondrites designated H, L, and LL.

Stone Meteorites: Carbonaceous Chondrites

Highly oxidized, containing organic compounds, and divided into five classes (CM, CR, CO, CV, CK), there is little in the world of meteorites that fascinates like the carbonaceous chondrites. A rare and particularly ancient sub-group, some have been found to contain water, carbon and even amino acids, suggesting they may have originally brought the building blocks of life to Earth. They are *undifferentiated* meaning they have undergone little change since forming in the early days of the solar system. Carbonaceous chondrites are typically very low in iron and often display enthralling chondrules when prepared in the lab. Allende, which fell in 1969, contains calcium, aluminum, and even tiny diamonds! (See page 15).

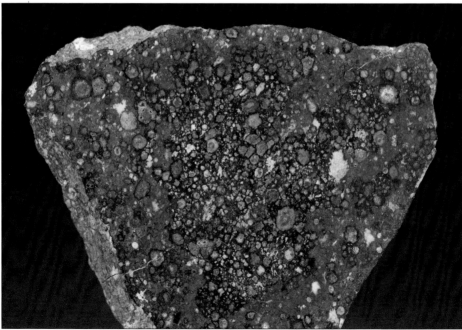

[top] Detail of densely-packed, colorful chondrules in the LL3.8 chondrite Northwest Africa (NWA) 5793. [above] While is has the same classification as Allende, the CV3.2 Northwest Africa (NWA) 7678 looks very different on the inside. Allende and NWA 7678 both display CAIs (calcium-aluminum inclusions in the form of non-spherical grey-white zones), but while Allende's interior is monochromatic, lab prepared sections of NWA 7678 display a brilliant kaleidoscope of tiny, multi-billion-year-old chondrules that came into existence at the very birth of our solar system. I find it among the most alluring of all meteorites.

[above] Allende is a carbonaceous chondrite (CV3.2) that fell in Chihuahua, Mexico on February 8, 1969. Often described as "the most studied meteorite in history," its massive nighttime fireball was seen by hundreds of witnesses in rural Mexico. Pieces were picked up by locals the next morning and many were acquired by Dr. Elbert King, who designed NASA's Lunar Receiving Lab from the Apollo era. Allende contains carbon and microscopic diamonds, believed to be the last remnants of an exploding sun that predates our own solar system. As such, at an estimated 12 billion years, they are the oldest things any human has ever touched. Note the coarse, matte, sandpaper-like fusion crust, and a few spherical chondrules visible on the surface. Pieces are still occasionally found today in the Allende strewnfield.

Stone Meteorites: Other Chondrite Classes

Enstatite chondrites contain unusual sulfide minerals and take the classifications EH and EL. The R chondrites, a very rare group, are high in iron-rich olivine and are named after the Rumuruti stone, which was seen to fall in Kenya on January 28, 1934.

Stone Meteorites: Achondrites

Achondrites are similar to volcanic rocks from Earth and are "without chondrules," hence their name. Igneous activity within the parent bodies where they formed caused melting and recrystallization that eradicated all traces of ancient chondrules. The most recognizable of the achondrites are the eucrites. Likely formed of basaltic crust, they are, essentially, volcanic rock from outer space and evidence the fact that some large asteroids have (or had) molten cores and experienced geologic upheavals much like our own planet. Fresh specimens often display a remarkable glossy black fusion

15

crust which looks almost like sprayed-on enamel paint. Together with howardites and diogenites, eucrites comprise the HED group of meteorites and are believed to have originated from within the large asteroid Vesta.

Most achondrites contain little or no iron, making them much more difficult to find than other meteorite types. They will not attract to a magnet or register on a metal detector. Since the vast majority of meteorites are iron-rich, we usually discount any specimens that fail to adhere to a magnet, unless they clearly show fusion crust, or were found under circumstances that suggest they are extraterrestrial in nature or were seen to fall.

Stone Meteorites: Moon And Mars Rocks

Do we really find lunar and martian rocks on the surface of our own planet? The answer is yes, but they are extremely rare. Only about 100 different lunar meteorites (lunaites) and approximately 40 martian meteorites have been discovered on Earth, and they all belong to the achondrite group. Impacts on the lunar and martian surfaces by other meteorites fired fragments into space and some of those fragments eventually fell on Earth.

In financial terms, lunar and martian specimens are among the most valuable meteorites, sometimes selling on the collectors market for as much as $1,000 per gram, making them worth many times their weight in gold.

[above] Eucrites, such as this Camel Donga from Australia, are extremely rare. They do not contain chondrules and have little, if any, metal. They are far lighter in weight than most other meteorites and will not adhere to even a powerful magnet. Note the shiny black fusion crust, reminiscent of enamel paint.

When the Apollo space program commenced in the 1960s, the engineers and astronauts involved could hardly have imagined that their work would have remarkable and far-reaching implications for meteorite science, as well as astronomy, geology, cosmology, and spaceflight. The challenge, to "land a man on the Moon and [return] him safely to the Earth," was delivered to a surprised world in late May of 1961 by President John F. Kennedy, six weeks after Yuri Gagarin became the first human in space. And just eight years later, Buzz Aldrin and Neil Armstrong landed a strange bug-like craft, *Eagle*, in the Sea of Tranquility on the surface of our nearest celestial neighbor — the Moon. But "near" seems like a poor choice of words, as it was nearly a half-million-mile round trip for Aldrin, Armstrong, and their Command Module pilot, Mike Collins. Apollo 11 was the first of six missions that returned lunar material to our Earth, where it was studied by NASA at the Lunar Receiving Center, designed by Dr. Elbert King, himself an authority on meteorites. That first mission returned about fifty specimens of lunar material, including rocks and dust.

If you look at the surface of the Moon through a telescope, you will immediately notice that its surface is partially covered by craters. Some of these may be volcanic in origin, but many or most are meteorite craters and they were made when meteorites from elsewhere — likely the asteroid belt — crashed into the Moon. As Dr. Randy Korotev, an expert on lunar meteorites at the Washington University in Saint Louis says:

[above left] An as-found specimen of the lunar meteorite Northwest Africa (NWA) 11303. The red patches are a result of terrestrial weathering. [above right] A full slice of the same meteorite, after cutting and polishing in the laboratory. The abundant fragments, cemented together, identify it as a *breccia*.

"Any rock on the lunar surface that is accelerated by the impact of a meteoroid to lunar escape velocity or greater will leave the moon's gravitational influence. Most rocks ejected from the moon become captured by the gravitational field of either the Earth or the Sun and go into orbit around these bodies ... Over a period of a few years to tens of thousands of years, those orbiting the Earth eventually fall to Earth."

When meteorite hunters find a new meteorite, they are often able to identify it from surface features or other characteristics, but cannot usually determine its composition without a laboratory examination. In other words, we know it is a space rock, but we don't know what type or where it may come from until we look at its internal structure in the lab.

Lunar meteorites, or lunaites, are very different in composition from the majority of other space rocks. Their uniqueness helps identify them as being lunar in origin. Most meteorites originate within asteroids, and most meteorites of asteroidal origin are rich in iron and nickel. But lunar

left] Astronaut Charlie Duke collecting specimens on the surface of the Moon during the 1972 Apollo 16 mission. nformation gathered from the samples he and the other moonwalkers brought back helped us identify lunar meteorites that landed on Earth. [above] The Lunar Receiving Lab in Houston was designed to study, in a safe environment, moon rocks brought back to Earth by the Apollo astronauts. The lab was the idea of NASA's)r. Elbert King, himself a meteorite expert who visited the Allende fall site in Mexico in February of 1969. n this photo, technicians examine fine powder returned from the Moon by the Apollo 14 mission in 1971.

meteorites show little or no metal and typically contain the minerals pyroxene, olivine, and plagioclase. While we may be able to tell just by eye that lunar meteorites are meteorites, it is because of the Apollo missions that we are able to identify their point of origin as the Moon. When the composition of a lunar meteorite is analyzed in the laboratory, it is clearly seen to be a match for specimens brought back to Earth by the Apollo astronauts. More remarkable than that, even, is the fact that some lunar meteorites can be paired with a particular part of our nearest neighbor, meaning we can tell not just that they came from the Moon, but also which part of the Moon. An example of this is Northwest Africa (NWA) 6355, a lunar meteorite found in 2010 with a total known weight of only 760 grams. Its composition bears a remarkable similarity to specimens returned by the Apollo 16 mission in April of 1972, commanded by John Young, which landed in the lunar highlands.

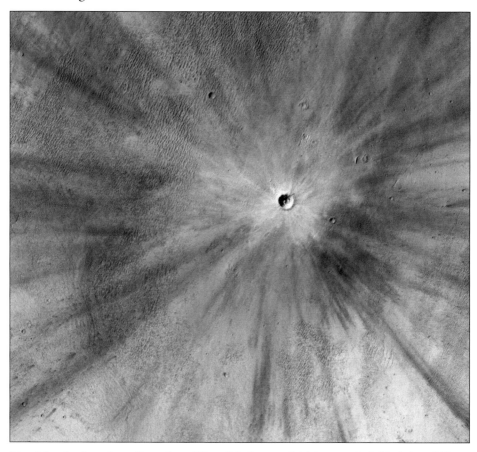

[above] A meteorite crater on the surface of Mars. Note the rays of debris — an ejecta blanket — which likely scattered meteorite fragments a considerable distance from the site of impact. Craters such as this one could have been responsible for blasting rocks into space; material which eventually landed on Earth as meteorites from Mars. This image has been enhanced using filters, and the color balance was designed to simulate the natural colors or Mars. Image credit: NASA/JPL/USGS

[above] This remarkable stone is a complete meteorite from Mars. Weighing 37.8 grams, it is designated as Northwest Africa (NWA) 6963 and was found in Morocco in 2011. The rounded surface, visually reminiscent of a stone axe head, was caused by ablation in Earth's atmosphere.

Since we have not yet sent human astronauts to the surface of Mars, we cannot study rock samples that have been returned to us from the Red Planet. The story of how we identify martian meteorites is, therefore, different from their lunar cousins, but no less fascinating.

It had long been observed by researchers that SNC meteorites were different from all others recovered on Earth. The class takes its name from the initial letters of three definitive martian meteorites: Shergotty (fell, India 1865), Nakhla (fell, Egypt 1911), and Chassigny (fell, France 1815). It was not until 1983 that the origin point of SNCs was discovered, and in the most surprising manner. Gasses trapped inside the Antarctic meteorite EET79001 were analyzed and found to be very similar to the martian atmosphere as measured by the Viking robot landers which landed on the Red Planet in 1976. This was confirmed by further study of the martian atmosphere (specifically, argon) by the Mars Curiosity rover in 2013.

Lunar and martian meteorites contain little or no iron and are very different from most other meteorites, both in terms of composition and visual characteristics. As such, their identification requires a great deal of expertise and specialized lab equipment. Washington University in St. Louis has an excellent, entertaining, and informative website about the identification of lunar meteorites. It was written by specialist Dr. Randy Korotev and is highly recommended if you wish to learn more on the subject.

STONY-IRON METEORITES

The rarest of the three main types, the stony-irons, account for less than 2% of all known meteorites. They originate on asteroids and are comprised of roughly equal amounts of nickel-iron and silicate. Stony-irons are divided into two subgroups: *mesosiderites* and *pallasites*. Due to high iron content, both types will adhere strongly to a magnet and register on a metal detector. I have found several massive stony-irons in the 100 to 200-lb range. Some of them were very deeply buried, but still produced an extremely loud and clear signal on the metal detector. Stony-irons usually have fascinating internal structures and often benefit from being cut, polished, and prepared in the laboratory to show off their inner beauty.

[above] The author and famed meteorite hunter Steve Arnold with a complete pallasite meteorite weighing an amazing 124 kg (273 lbs) found near Brenham, Kansas in 2008 while filming the *Meteorite Men* adventure television series for Discovery networks. This meteorite was located at a depth of nearly 2 meters (6 feet) using a very large pulse induction metal detector (see page 104), pulled behind an ATV. The mass was so large it had to be removed from the ground using a backhoe. [top left] A small specimen of the Admire pallasite after cleaning and preparation in the lab. Loose, oxidized surface material has been removed, leaving a shiny nickel-iron matrix peppered with brightly-colored olivine crystals. [bottom left] A large example of the same meteorite, prior to cleaning. When I pulled this mass out of a field in the American Midwest, opaque olivine crystals were clearly visible on the meteorite's surface. Green or brown crystals on the exterior of a suspected meteorite, together with strong attraction to a magnet, can be an indicator that you have found a pallasite.

Stony-Iron Meteorites: Mesosiderites

The mesosiderites are the smaller of the two stony-iron groups. They contain both nickel-iron and silicates and usually show an attractive, high-contrast, silver and black matrix when cut and polished. The seemingly random mixture of inclusions can lead to some very striking features. The word mesosiderite is derived from the Greek for "half," and "iron," and they are very rare. Of the tens of thousands of officially cataloged meteorites, less than 100 are mesosiderites. From the outside, mesosiderites often look and feel much like iron meteorites; they are dense and will feel heavier than expected for their size. The exterior will likely be oxidized and crystals are not visible on the surface. When cut and polished, the interior will typically show very bright and randomly distributed patches of metal, reminiscent of steel. Mesosiderites will attract very strongly to a magnet.

Mesosiderites are believed to have been formed by a catastrophic impact when two asteroids with different compositions collided in deep space.

Stony-Iron Meteorites: Pallasites

Pallasites are perhaps the most alluring of all meteorites, and they are certainly of great interest to private collectors. Pallasites consist of a nickel-iron matrix rich in colorful olivine crystals.

When olivine crystals are of sufficient purity and display an emerald-green color, they are known as the gemstone peridot. Pallasites take their name from a German zoologist and explorer, Peter Pallas, who described the first-known pallasite — the Russian meteorite Krasnojarsk, which was found in the eighteenth century near the Siberian capital of the same name. When cut and polished into thin slabs, the crystals in pallasites become translucent, giving them a remarkable otherworldly beauty.

While micro-diamonds have been found in some meteorites, notably the carbonaceous chondrite Allende, pallasites are the only meteorites that contain gemstones easily visible to the naked eye. The crystals in most pallasites, however, are shocked, meaning they show fractures and would be regarded as imperfect by gemologists. The crystals in the Admire pallasite are extremely rare in that they do not show shock features. A number of these crystals were extracted by my team, and faceted gem experts. The resulting extraterrestrial gemstones are exquisite, and far more rare than diamonds.

The high iron content in pallasites (typically about 50%) means they will attract strongly to a magnet, register clearly on a metal detector, and their surfaces will usually look much like those of iron meteorites. Pallasites that have been on Earth for a long time may show a particularly bright, rusty orange exterior. Close examination of an uncleaned or as-found pallasite may well reveal weathered green olivine crystals on the surface (see photo on page 18), which can help with identification in the field.

[far left] The magnificent Vaca Muerta, Chile mesosiderite found on my 2010 expedition to the Atacama Desert. This piece was so dense, I thought at first that it may have been man-made iron. Note the high contrast between the nickel-iron matrix (silver) and the silicate inclusions (black) which is a typical characteristic of mesosiderites. [left] A full slice of the Brahin pallasite from Russia, after being prepared in the laboratory. This stony-iron has a very high abundance of olivine crystals and it has been backlit to show their translucency. Note the variance in crystal colors: yellow, orange, green, and brown. Olivine crystals are naturally green, but terrestrial weathering can cause their hue to change.

HOW TO IDENTIFY METEORITES
IN THE LABORATORY AND IN THE FIELD

It takes knowledge, practice, and experience to tell the difference between a meteorite and an Earth rock. This fact is demonstrated time and time again by poorly-researched newspaper interviews with people who think they have found a space rock. The typical story goes something like this: A man is walking his dog or driving home at night and sees a bright fireball in the sky. He is convinced that it landed "just over there." The next day he goes out searching, finds a strange-looking rock in a field or driveway, and calls the local newspaper to report that he has found a meteorite. A few inaccurate articles are published and then, eventually, the rock gets taken to a specialist who determines that it is not a meteorite, but rather basalt, or hematite, or cement, or old iron slag from a smelter. The witness really did see a fireball, but he did not know how to recognize a meteorite on the ground, so he picked up the first unusual terrestrial rock he saw, mistaking it for a meteorite.

It may seem obvious, but it needs stating: If you want to find meteorites, you need to know exactly what to look for. Most meteorites show high density; the vast majority contain a great deal of iron and will easily adhere to a strong magnet. Meteorites generally look and feel different from the Earth rocks around them. They do not contain the common mineral quartz, and, in general, do not contain *vesicles*—small pinprick holes in the surface of a rock caused when gas escapes from cooling molten material (see page 46). The volcanic rock pumice, often used in skin care for the removal of callouses, contains vesicles, which is one reason why it is very light in weight. If your suspected meteorite looks like a sponge with tiny holes on its surface, it is probably volcanic rock or slag of earthly origin.

METEORITE IDENTIFICATION: THE MAGNET TEST

The vast majority of meteorites contain a significant amount of extraterrestrial iron and nickel, so the first step in identifying most types of possible meteorites is the magnet test. Iron and stony-iron meteorites are especially rich in iron, and will stick to a powerful magnet so strongly that it can be difficult to separate them. Stone meteorites, for the most part, also have a high iron content (often about 20%) and a good magnet will adhere to them as well. Many Earth rocks will also be attracted to a magnet, so this is not a definitive test, but it is a step in the right direction. It is worth noting that

[left] Excavating a deeply-buried iron meteorite in the Muonionalusta strewnfield, north of the Arctic Circle in Sweden. The glacial moraine in which the Muonionalusta irons are found also contains terrestrial iron oxides which often register on a metal detector and can confuse the hunter. This substantial 46-pound meteorite was found using a sophisticated Lorenz Deepmax detector with a range of over 2 meters (6 ft).

[top] The vast majority of meteorites contain iron and will easily adhere to a good magnet. These weathered stone fragments I found in Nevada had been sitting on a dry lake bed for tens of thousands of years, yet still had enough iron content to jump onto my magnet. [above left] Detail of fusion crust on the carbonaceous chondrite Allende, which fell in Chihuahua, Mexico, on February 8, 1969. This specimen was picked up immediately after the fall and shows no weathering. [above right] Fusion crust is fragile and will eventually erode. Note the weathering cracks clearly visible on a different piece of the same meteorite, picked up several years later. [right] I found this 27-kg (59-lb) iron, nicknamed the "Brenham Buffalo," while hunting in Kiowa County, Kansas. We were looking for Brenham pallasites but unexpectedly found several large siderites (irons) as well. They were from the same fall, but demonstrated different visual characteristics and this clearly illustrates why the successful meteorite hunter must always be alert, adaptive, and resourceful. The meteorite you find may not be the one you were originally looking for. This iron is so dense that the toaster-sized specimen pictured weighs approximately the same as an eight-year-old child!

meteorites will show a uniform attraction to a magnet, whereas terrestrial rocks will often demonstrate a greater attraction on one face.

Lunar and martian meteorites, and most achondrites (stone meteorites without chondrules), contain little or no iron and even a powerful magnet will generally have no effect upon them. These meteorite types, however, are so rare that, as a general rule, we discount specimens that will not adhere to a magnet, especially if they do not exhibit fusion crust.

METEORITE IDENTIFICATION: WEIGHT AND DENSITY

Iron is heavy and that means the majority of meteorites are heavy. Due to the high iron content (20 – 93%) of most meteorites, they feel significantly weightier in the hand than an ordinary Earth rock. A softball-sized iron meteorite will likely weigh between six and eight pounds, making it seem unnaturally dense. Imagine holding a steel ball bearing the size of a grapefruit and you will get an idea of the density of iron meteorites.

VISUAL IDENTIFICATION: FUSION CRUST

When a meteoroid streaks through our atmosphere, tremendous heat is generated by atmospheric resistance. The surface of the rock melts and the air around it incandesces. As a result of this brief but intense heating, the surface forms a thin, dark rind called fusion crust. This crust makes meteorites appear darker than most terrestrial rocks around them. A freshly-fallen stone meteorite with intact fusion crust will look as black as a charcoal briquette. Desert varnish forms on the surface of some Earth rocks, particularly in arid areas, and can easily be mistaken for fusion crust by an untrained eye. True fusion crust does not occur on terrestrial rocks. It is delicate and will oxidize or weather away over time, so stone meteorites that have been on Earth for long periods of time often have a dark reddish color. Fusion crust also forms on irons and stony-irons, but it is fragile and tends to oxidize quickly.

[above] A fusion-crusted stone meteorite from the Ash Creek, Texas, fall of February 15, 2009. Note how the stone acquired light brown streaks of mud when it hit the ground. It was picked up right after the fall, so its fusion crust is still black (fresh). [top right] A complete stone meteorite found in the Sahara. The color and shape are typical of chondrites that have been on Earth for many years. [right] Old Camp Wash is an excellent example of what to look for. This large stone meteorite, weighing 13.85 kg (30.5 lbs), was found by a rancher and brought to Aerolite Meteorites for identification. Although found continents apart, note the striking similarity in color to the San Juan meteorite from Chile, pictured on page 13.

VISUAL IDENTIFICATION: REGMAGLYPTS

Regmaglypts, also known as "thumbprints," are oval depressions of varying size found on the surface of many meteorites. These indentations resemble the marks a sculptor might make with his thumbs on a wet lump of clay, hence their name. The size of regmaglypts on a particular meteorite is usually proportional to the size of the meteorite itself. A 100-gram iron may be covered with scores of tiny thumbprints, each just a few millimeters in length, while a 100-kilogram meteorite might display regmaglypts that are each several inches in length. Regmaglypts, created as a meteoroid's outer layer melts during flight, are another feature unique to space rocks.

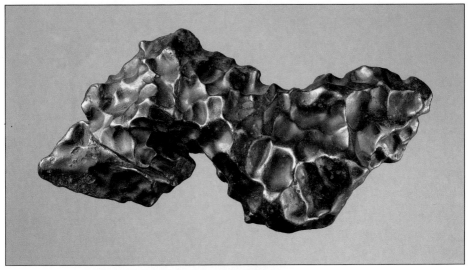

[above] Multiple fine, well-formed, overlapping regmaglypts on this 204-gram Sikhote-Alin iron meteorite identify this is a whole individual, rather than a fragment. [left] Regmaglypts are most frequently seen on iron meteorites, but they can also occur on stone meteorites, as demonstrated by this excellent 828.6-gram example of the Juancheng meteorite which fell in China in 1997. This specimen was found some years after the fall, and the once-black fusion crust has weathered to grey, with some slight traces of rust. [far left] Details of regmaglypts on three different cleaned and uncleaned iron meteorites.

VISUAL IDENTIFICATION: FLOW LINES

As a meteoroid hurtles through our atmosphere, its surface may melt and flow in tiny rivulets known as *flow lines*. The patterns formed by flow lines can be minute, often thinner than a strand of human hair, and they are one of the most unique and intriguing surface characteristics of meteorites.

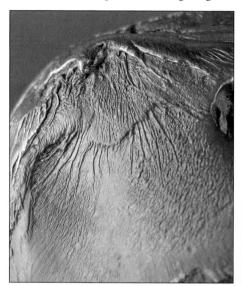 

[top left] This magnified image shows a network of tiny overlapping flow lines on the nose of a highly oriented Sikhote-Alin iron. [top right] Delicate flow lines on the leading edge of a Taza (NWA 859) iron meteorite. [above] Long, fine flow lines and shiny black fusion crust are often seen on the surface of eucrites (achondrites which contain little or no metal). This Millbillillie eucrite fell in Australia in 1960.

VISUAL IDENTIFICATION: ORIENTATION

Most meteoroids spin and tumble as they plummet through the atmosphere. Occasionally, one will maintain a fixed orientation towards the surface of our planet, causing the leading edge to ablate into a shield, nose cone, or bullet shape. When meteorites ablate, some of their mass is removed as a result of vaporization. Meteorites which display such features are rare and are described as oriented.

[top] Steve Arnold with the massive 3/4-ton meteorite he unearthed in Kansas in 2005. It is the largest oriented pallasite in the world and the largest meteorite ever found in the Brenham strewnfield. Photograph © Arnold Meteorites [above left] This highly-oriented Sikhote-Alin iron acquired a shield shape as a result of ablation during flight. [above right] An oriented stone meteorite found in the Sahara Desert.

VISUAL IDENTIFICATION: ROLLOVER LIPS

A typical oriented meteorite will have a convex leading edge and a flat or concave trailing edge. Sometimes molten material will flow onto the trailing edge during flight, creating a fine, yet distinct feature known as a *rollover lip*. This intriguing characteristic provides a glimpse into the processes that give meteorites their unique shapes and features.

[top] Bassikounou is an H5 chondrite that fell near Hodh Ech in Mauritania on October 16, 2006. This 12.1-gram oriented individual shows a very distinct rollover lip. Note, also, the rich, black fusion crust, indicative of a recent fall. [above] An oriented 27-gram Sikhote-Alin iron with a 100% rollover lip on the trailing edge. Complete rollover lips such as this are a rare and intriguing feature on meteorites.

VISUAL IDENTIFICATION: CHONDRULES AND METAL FLAKES

Stone meteorites known as chondrites are the most abundant meteorite type. They are composed largely of chondrules, which are tiny, grain-like spheroids, often of widely differing colors. Chondrules are believed to have formed in the solar nebula disk before the planets in our solar system and are not present in Earth rocks. Chondrites are usually also rich in metal flakes of nickel-iron. Shiny blobs of this extraterrestrial alloy are sometimes visible on their surfaces, although you may need a hand lens to see them. A simple identification test involves removing a small corner of a suspected stone meteorite with a file or bench grinder and examining the exposed face with a loupe. If the interior displays metal flakes and small, round, colorful inclusions, it may well be the real thing. Carrying a small metal file with you in the field can assist in chondrite identification. A small "window" in a suspected meteorite, and inspection with a loupe or magnifying lens, will make it easy to identify chondrules if they are present. Be careful when grinding a window as excessive cutting can damage a specimen, thereby decreasing its value and aesthetic appeal.

[above] When a prospector stumbled across the El Boludo strewnfield in Mexico while searching for gold nuggets, he brought his finds to me. The exterior surfaces were weathered and I was not 100% sure it was a meteorite. I ground off a corner and immediately saw abundant metallic flakes and relict (altered) chondrules which told me, without doubt, that it was a stone meteorite and likely an ordinary chondrite.

LAB TESTING OF METEORITES: NICKEL CONTENT

Nickel is rare on Earth but always present in iron and stony-iron meteorites. If a suspected meteorite passes the magnet test, and looks promising following a visual inspection, we may elect to conduct a test for nickel. Assay labs can perform an analysis of the nickel content for a modest fee, but it is necessary to cut off a small sample in order to perform such a test. Some labs and universities with meteorite departments can perform much more sophisticated tests without damaging a specimen. For example, the Ion Beam Analysis of Materials (IBeAM) laboratory at the Center for Meteorite Studies at Arizona State University uses accelerated ions to determine, with great accuracy, the composition of samples. In simple terms, that means we can discover the chemical makeup of a specimen without slicing it in half. The IBeAM can perform an analysis from a tiny cut sample, and the results appear on a computer screen within a few seconds.

We only use the nickel test on suspected iron or stony-iron meteorites. The nickel content in stone meteorites is very low and not used as an indicator. We expect the nickel content in an iron meteorite to be 3% or more, with 7% being typical. The nickel-iron matrix of a stony-iron should contain a similar percentage but, since stony-irons are roughly half silicate in composition, an average overall percentage might be about 3%.

A rare subclass of iron meteorites, the *ataxites*, is characterized by high nickel content. The Tishomingo ataxite, for example, discovered in 1965 in Oklahoma, is extremely unusual in that it consists of 32.5% nickel.

[left] This suspected stone meteorite was cut but not polished, in order to conduct a simple visual test. The bright metal flakes and abundant light-colored spherical chondrules clearly identify it as an ordinary chondrite (stone meteorite). Once we have a positive identification we will decide if the find circumstances warrant sending a particular meteorite to an accredited lab for full classification.

HOW MUCH ARE METEORITES WORTH?

The scientific importance of meteorites cannot be over emphasized. They have great research value to academics, and financial value to collectors.

Meteorites may have spent millions of years traveling through the vacuum of space at temperatures approaching absolute zero. After landing on our planet, they are immediately exposed to oxygen and moisture, and the process of terrestrialization begins. Iron starts to oxidize and delicate fusion crust will begin to corrode. The sooner a fresh fall is delivered into the hands of a researcher, the more valuable it is to science. There is a real urgency to recover new falls and get them to a lab as quickly as possible, where measuring the decay of radioactive isotopes can provide important scientific information.

Much like other collectibles—comic books, baseball cards, stamps, coins, or fine art—the financial value of meteorites is determined by a range of factors including rarity of type, condition, and aesthetic appeal. On the collectors market, meteorites are generally sold by weight, and measured using the metric system. While there is a fairly well-established average price for some of the more widely available meteorite types, a specimen that has a remarkable story attached to it — such as the Peekskill stone that hit a parked car in New York state in 1992 — or a piece that is visually pleasing will command a higher value.

Meteorite prices vary just like any other collectible. A survey of the market in 2019 showed unclassified stone chondrites, picked up by nomads

[left] A premium quality Sikhote-Alin iron meteorite exhibiting beautiful surface features, such as the example pictured, is worth thousands of dollars on the collectors market.

[above] Iron meteorites on display in a glass cabinet at the Denver Mineral Show, in front of a solar system backdrop. The Denver show takes place every September in Colorado. Visiting vendors and exhibits is a good way to familiarize yourself with meteorites and meet other collectors and enthusiasts, and most of the best shows offer free admission.

wandering in the Sahara Desert, available for about $0.80/gram. Attractive stones from a witnessed fall, such as Gao-Guenie (Burkina Faso, Africa, March 5, 1960) could be purchased for about $1.50/gram and a good quality one-kilogram specimen of the Campo del Cielo iron meteorite from Chaco Province, Argentina, might sell for about $1,000 ($1.00/gram).

The Russian iron Sikhote-Alin fall of February 12, 1947 is the largest single meteorite event in modern recorded history. Individuals—meteorite specimens which landed as one intact piece, rather than exploding on or near the ground—are typically well-preserved and demonstrate marvelous sculptural qualities and surface features. A premium Sikhote-Alin specimen will carry a price tag of $3 to $4/gram.

Pallasites are packed with olivine (the gemstone peridot) and are highly desirable when cut and polished because of the alluring color and translucency of the crystals they contain. Prepared slices of the most attractive pallasites such as Imilac (Chile), Glorieta Mountain (New Mexico), and Esquel (Argentina) are prized for their colorful gemstones and long-term stability and will fetch between $30 and $50/gram. A quality and well-prepared pallasite slice about the size of a small dinner plate will have a price tag in the thousands of dollars.

At the high end of the pricing scale are unusual types such as the diogenite Tatahouine (fell June 27, 1931, Foum Tatahouine, Tunisia).

A prime specimen will easily fetch $50/gram, while rare examples of lunar and martian meteorites have sold for $1,000/gram or more—about 25 times the current price of gold.

When valuing meteorites, the price per gram usually goes down as a specimen's size increases. In other words, an attractive 50-gram example of the Gibeon iron from Namibia might be worth $75 to a collector, which equates to $1,500/kg. A 30-kg mass of the same meteorite might sell for $1000/kg, or two-thirds the gram price of a smaller piece.

These numbers are just an approximation. Values are influenced by many factors including condition, provenance, and aesthetic appearance. For example, a meteorite that comes with an interesting, old label or identification card from a famous museum is usually considerably more valuable than a comparable specimen with no recorded history of ownership (provenance).

If you find a meteorite, the most important thing is to determine if it is new to science and/or might have scientific value. Once you have carried out your field tests with a magnet and magnifying lens, consider sending it—or a piece of it—to a university with a meteoritics department. Once a new meteorite find has been studied, classified, and named (see Chapter 15), it is actually worth more to the finder because it will have been included in the online directory of all known meteorites, The Meteoritical Bulletin Database.

Meteorites are worth money and a new discovery can provide substantial income for the finder and/or landowner. In 2006, a Kansas landowner contacted me. He had found a large unusual rock, weighing about 36 kg (79 lbs), on his property. After looking at some photos, I was reasonably sure that he had a real space rock. At my request he sent me a small sample, and the minute I saw it, I knew it was a genuine meteorite. A cut face displayed abundant chondrules, and it also adhered strongly to a magnet. I sent the sample on to a meteoriticist who performed a detailed lab analysis. The new find was classified as an H5 chondrite, and given the official name of Coffeyville. I assisted the finder in having his find cut into slices in order to display its interesting interior, and the resulting sales were in the thousands of dollars. Sometimes even an accidental find can generate good revenue.

A similar thing happened in 2015 with the Old Camp Wash meteorite (see page 31). The finder was patrolling his property on an ATV when he saw a hefty orange-brown rock that seemed out of place. A regular viewer of *Meteorite Men*, he was familiar with what meteorites look like, and contacted Aerolite Meteorites. His rock turned out to be a completely new discovery. Aerolite purchased the mass from him, got it named and classified, and (with his permission) conducted a thorough search of the find area, which yielded additional pieces. Old Camp Wash is just one of many new meteorites that came to light as a direct result of the *Meteorite Men* television series.

METEORWRONGS, HOT ROCKS, AND HOW THEY WILL HELP YOU BECOME A BETTER HUNTER

Years ago I added a detailed section to the Aerolite Meteorites website (www.aerolite.org), with tips on how to identify meteorites. It includes photographs of Earth rocks and genuine meteorites, along with some simple tests that finders can carry out at home. Our "Aerolite Guide to Meteorite Identification" proved so popular that people began sending us suspected meteorites, and a number of them turned out to be the real thing. In some cases, the finder was just curious and wanted to keep the meteorite in his or her collection. In other instances, we helped the finder get the new space rock classified, named, inducted into the official literature and, eventually, sold for good money. We have also received an enormous assortment of "meteorwrongs"—Earth rocks that look like meteorites but are not. Some of those rocks were intriguing and the finders kept them even though they were not meteorites. We were instructed to discard others which had no value, and they now happily populate my unusual-looking rock garden.

[above] The common terrestrial iron oxide hematite is often mistaken for meteorites by novices. Hematite typically does not show any attraction to a magnet and will usually leave a red streak on a white ceramic tile, while an iron meteorite will leave little or no streak. The surface features on some hematite specimens also have a visual resemblance to regmaglypts. [left] An unexploded artillery shell, discovered while meteorite hunting in Chile's Atacama Desert. Ammunition, live or expended, will register clearly on a metal detector, so unexploded ordnance can be a hazard for the meteorite hunter.

[left] A World War II-era 50-caliber machine gun cartridge found lying where it fell on a military testing range of the salt flats in Utah. [top] Unexploded artillery shell. The color of corroded steel is very similar to oxidized iron meteorites. [above] A massive unexploded warhead from the Vietnam era, estimated to weigh 2,000 pounds. My team found this while searching for meteorites in a remote area and reported its location to the USAF, which reportedly blew it up on the spot. Meteorite hunting *can* be hazardous.

I have been sent flint, chalk, basalt, granite, limestone, lead, copper ore, iron slag, and even man-made glass by people who thought they had found meteorites. The terrestrial rocks most commonly mistaken for meteorites are the iron oxides magnetite and hematite, along with lava and slag (see below). Magnetite can be particularly tricky as it is often metallic-looking, heavy for its size, and typically adheres well to a magnet. It is not quite dense enough to be a typical meteorite, however, and with a practiced eye the attentive hunter will learn to distinguish magnetite from meteorites.

Another common meteorwrong is botryoidal hematite (see page 43). This common stone displays a reddish tint that sometimes appears burned or melted, and often has a rounded, almost bubbly surface that looks — to the untrained observer — as if it could have fallen, burning, from the sky. The term botryoidal, derived from the Greek, means, loosely, "like a bunch of grapes." It is actually a collection of iron oxide spheres formed by the radial deposition of mineral material around nuclei. This commonly misidentified rock typically has little or no attraction to a magnet.

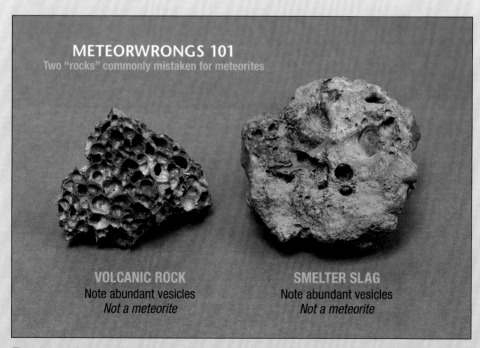

METEORWRONGS 101
Two "rocks" commonly mistaken for meteorites

VOLCANIC ROCK
Note abundant vesicles
Not a meteorite

SMELTER SLAG
Note abundant vesicles
Not a meteorite

There is a good reason why igneous rocks (cooled lava) and slag (a man-made residue from smelting) look as if they were once molten. They *were!* But that molten state was a result of nature or industry here on Earth, rather than high-velocity travel through our atmosphere. When lava and slag cool, they release gas, which forms surface holes called vesicles. While a very few meteorites have been shown to include small vesicles, they are rare, microscopic, and typically part of the interior structure. Meteorites do not exhibit multiple vesicles on the surface such as those pictured in these two examples. Both of these "wrongs" were sent to me by people who thought they had found meteorites. Rocks like these are very frequently mistaken for meteorites by hopeful hunters who have not done their research.

If you want to really understand meteorites, buy a couple of inexpensive specimens for study. Canyon Diablo (Arizona) is an excellent example of a somewhat terrestrialized iron meteorite, and a modest-sized piece can be easily obtained for less than $50. Unclassified stone meteorites from Northwest Africa — often called NWA XXX — are also affordable and relatively abundant on the collectors market. If you are serious about finding your own space rocks, buy a stone meteorite and an iron meteorite from a reputable dealer and familiarize yourself with how they look and feel, and listen to what they sound like under your metal detector. These are great investments. Take them out into the field with you. I call them "throw stones," because I will actually throw them on the ground to see what meteorites look like, in that environment and that light. Your eyes become attuned to the color and shape of meteorites, and you can also practice with your metal detector. The more you train, the better accustomed your ears will become to the sounds that buried meteorites make on your unit.

METEORWRONGS ARE, LITERALLY, EVERYWHERE

If you are going to start hunting for meteorites, one thing I can guarantee is you are going to find meteorwrongs. Your metal detector can only tell you so much; you need to do the rest.

Metal detectors that are used for hunting meteorites are calibrated to return a signal when they find iron. Sophisticated modern hand-held detectors have the capability to distinguish between different types of metal.

The Fisher F75, for example, employs a digital readout—from 1 to 100—that can help you identify, to some degree, the makeup of a buried target. Iron reads between 4 and 15 on the display panel, but iron does not always mean "meteorite." When I was hunting at the Henbury crater field in Australia, I quickly learned that a 13 on my control panel meant I had the real thing. One larger mass close to the surface read a 7, so when you are learning it is a good idea to dig and examine all ferrous targets. A very low reading on the scale, such as 3 or 4, is usually man-made refined iron, most likely nails or bolts. At the Brenham, Kansas, site the iron-rich pallasites that my team excavated read 11 on the meter, while stone meteorites from Buzzard Coulee gave us a 14, so there can be a significant variance in readings from one meteorite type to another.

Even though I have hunted for meteorites in some of the most remote places on Earth, it seems that, most of the time, someone has been there before me and carelessly left their trash. Wherever people lived, worked, farmed, or fought, they left things behind, and many of those things contain iron. While hunting at one site, I was right on top of the old Santa Fe Trail, which is full of lost and discarded items from wagon trains — all of them buried. I did a great deal of digging before finding a real meteorite.

Most man-made items are found in the top foot of soil, so the deeper you go, the better the chances that your target is not something that was fabricated by a human being. That is not always the case; sometimes trash is buried on purpose, and deeply. While filming the *Meteorite Men* pilot in Brenham, Kansas, we received a massive return signal from our giant metal detector (see page 105). We were inside the strewnfield and quite close to areas where large meteorites had been found in the past, so we were elated. We dug down a couple of feet, but did not uncover the target. Reasonably sure that we had a meteorite, we brought in a backhoe, only to find half an hour later that our "new find" was a 55-gallon oil drum that had, for some inexplicable reason, been buried deep in a field.

In 2009 I received special permission to hunt inside the small craters that surround the main structure at the Odessa meteorite site in Ector County, Texas. Those craters are actually the remains of dig holes where large meteorites were uncovered during the 1940s, and were not formed by the meteorites themselves. I thought it likely that some meteoritic material remained in the pits and, after getting a strong signal at the bottom of one of the pits, my team brought in a mechanical excavator. Excitement turned to dismay when we found that the old dig holes had been used as a dump and, instead of a meteorite, we unearthed a mass of old beer cans. They were all empty, which was no fun at all.

Items that I have found while hunting (most of them underground) include soda cans, sardine tins, horseshoes, frontier-era wagon wheels, plow blades, hubcaps, screwdrivers, animal traps, bolts, nails, hammers, wrenches, axe heads, Civil War Minié balls, batteries, a full clip of live ammunition for a .32 pistol, logging equipment, chains, a Wild West-era revolver, aircraft parts, tractor parts, a large crowbar, an uncapped oil well, shoes with iron heels, brass .50-caliber machine gun cartridges, sunglasses, keys, money, several unexploded bombs, artillery shells, and two very large missiles. It is worth noting that if you are digging targets near a military test range, or in areas that saw heavy combat in the modern era, such as northern Europe, there is always a chance that you will come across live ammunition or unexploded military ordnance. This has happened to me on at least five separate occasions, so use extra caution if you are working in such areas.

Picking up a meteorwrong from the surface is one thing; digging one up from several feet underground is another. It can be tiring and discouraging to spend half an hour toiling through hard ground with a muddy shovel only to reveal a foot of rusty pipe. That is why, when people ask me what you need in order to be a successful meteorite hunter, I say: "Determination."

Be prepared to dig up a lot of trash on your way to finding meteorites, especially in areas that have been farmed, mined, or were once settled.

HOT ROCKS

A "hot rock" is a terrestrial stone that sets off a metal detector. It is an old gold prospector's phrase that has been adopted by meteorite hunters. It is important to remember that there are many different types of Earth rocks that contain iron, so if your target turns out to be stone, rather than man-made iron trash, do not automatically assume it is a meteorite. This is when your ability to identify meteorites in the field will be most valuable: Does your find stick strongly to a magnet? Does it exhibit any of the visual characteristics we might expect to see, such as remnant fusion crust, regmaglypts, exposed chondrules, or metal flecks? The successful meteorite hunter is not only adept at finding and excavating targets, but also knows how to look for the telltale features that are unique to space rocks.

Some areas are rife with hot rocks; others will have none. The great Mundrabilla strewnfield in Australia contained no hot rocks at all—only thousands of square miles of limestone, which will not generate a return signal to a metal detector. If I received a signal, I knew it was either a meteorite or a piece of metallic trash, and since we were hunting in a remote location there was very little man-made trash present. In contrast, Arizona's Gold Basin strewnfield is so rich in hot rocks that—on my early hunts there, when I was relatively inexperienced—I dug up ten or twenty hot rocks for every meteorite.

A LEARNING EXPERIENCE

When I am finding and digging up meteorwrongs, I look at it as doing extra credit in meteorite hunting school. Each time you locate a target and dig it, you become a better detectorist. In time, you will be able to identify buried nails, barbed wire, fence staples, and some hot rocks solely by the unique sound they make through your detector's speaker.

When searching the Morasko, Poland crater field during 2011, I knew much of the site had already been meticulously hunted, with every single military relic and piece of trash collected and documented by the earlier team. That meant whenever I *did* get a target, I was almost certainly moving into an unhunted area. A single target did, several times, lead me to a pocket within the zone that had never been covered by detectors. That led to more targets and, in one spectacular case, a giant meteorite.

The more hours you spend in the field, the better a hunter you will become. Finding meteorites takes time and you should expect to dig up many "wrongs" before you locate a "right." Try to view every expedition and every dig—even if you only find cans and bullets—as a learning experience. My friend Sonny Clary, a dedicated and amazingly successful meteorite hunter, once said to me: "Every hour I spend in the field not finding anything brings me one hour closer to the find that I *do* make."

[top] When I found this stone meteorite, it had only been on the ground for a few days. Because it was part of a witnessed fireball, it is described as a "fall." [above] The Gold Basin L4 ordinary chondrite has been on Earth for an estimated 20,000 years and is described as a "find." It is weathered and resembles some terrestrial rocks in appearance, but it still displays remnant fusion crust, flow lines, and faint regmaglypts.

METEORITE FALLS VERSUS METEORITE FINDS

The novice meteorite hunter or collector might, understandably, be confused by the following exchange. A colleague calls me on the telephone and says: "I have a new stone meteorite for sale. Are you interested?" I reply: "Is it a fall or a find?"

Clearly, in order to recover a meteorite, you have to determine where it landed. All meteorites fell out of the sky at some point, but "fall" and "find" have specific meanings in the world of meteorites.

A fall refers to a *witnessed fall*—one or more meteorites that were actually seen in flight by credible observers, and the term is usually associated with fireballs. A fireball is a term used to describe a particularly large meteor.

A *find* is a meteorite that has been discovered on the ground, but is not part of a witnessed event. Falls are typically recent, while finds have often been on Earth for long periods of time. Witnessed falls tend to carry more financial value than finds, as they are forever associated with a particular time and place, may be documented by fireball footage, and sometimes have intriguing stories attached, such as the Claxton meteorite which hit a mailbox in Georgia in 1984. Finds could conceivably be recovered anywhere, whereas recovered falls are usually the result of ground searches following a documented fireball event.

Over the years, a number of finders have come to me with a single meteorite that they discovered while hiking, gold prospecting, or rock hounding. They almost always ask if they should go back and look for more. They want to know if the meteorite they found was the only one, or if others fell at the same time. The answer is we usually do not know. Sometimes only a single meteorite will fall; sometimes hundreds or even thousands of fragments rain down into one fall zone. The Lorton, Virginia meteorite is a perfect example of a solitary fall. On January 20, 2010, a single stone punched through the roof of a dentist's office and broke into several pieces. A thorough search of the surrounding area failed to turn up any additional pieces. The Sikhote-Alin fall (February 12, 1947, Siberia) scattered literally thousands of pieces over a forest in eastern Siberia, and meteorites continued to be found at the site for decades.

The only way to discover if your meteorite was part of a shower, or if it was just a single piece, is to carefully hunt the area surrounding the initial find. Meteorites appear to sometimes fall in small clusters, and Gold Basin (Arizona) is an excellent example of this phenomenon. I have hunted at the site for hours, even days, and not found a single meteorite. When I did eventually make a find, I meticulously searched the immediate area, and often found several more pieces in close proximity within only a few minutes.

If you find a meteorite that clearly shows a broken face, or is an angular fragment rather than a complete individual with a smooth, rounded surface, it is possible that the other pieces fell somewhere, perhaps nearby. Bear in mind that meteorites may fragment here on Earth long after a fall due to terrestrial weathering. Pieces can also be transported some distance away from their original fall site by natural processes such as floods, landslides, and other forms of erosion.

During their final stages of flight, after experiencing atmospheric braking, a meteorite might be traveling at 300 miles per hour. That is equivalent to about 440 feet per second, so if a meteorite explodes several miles above the ground, and the fragments begin traveling along only very slightly different flight paths, they could be widely dispersed by the time they reach the surface.

As a general rule, if I find a meteorite on the ground, I always hope and assume that it is just one of many. I recommend marking the exact find location with a small flag or GPS unit, then searching outwards in all directions in the hope of finding more.

[above] This is the single most important photograph in the entire book. Study it! It is a weathered stone meteorite weighing about 1 kg (2.2 lbs), *in situ*, untouched and exactly as it was found in the desert. Note the reddish-black hue. Note how very clearly it stands out from the terrestrial rocks surrounding it. This stone was easily visible from at least 15 meters (50 feet) away and gave a very loud signal when the metal detector was passed over it.

UNDERSTANDING AND
HUNTING STREWNFIELDS

When a meteoroid enters the atmosphere at high speed, it rapidly heats up and, if it is of sufficient size, will turn into a fireball. Consider this: That meteoroid has been traveling in space, nearly at absolute zero, for perhaps millions of years. When its surface begins to heat up, the temperature of the mass's exterior rises several thousand degrees in just a few seconds. When metal is heated, it expands. Combine that expansion with the tremendous atmospheric pressure the expanding mass suddenly encounters, and the result can be a very large explosion.

The great Russian meteoriticist E.L. Krinov suggested that the thousands of meteorites that hit the ground following the massive Sikhote-Alin fall may all have originally been part of a single, very large mass. As the mass fragmented, it dropped pieces ranging from one gram or less to hundreds of kilograms within a relatively small area. That zone, where multiple pieces from the same meteorite land at the same time, is known as a strewnfield. Understanding strewnfields is one of the most important lessons for the successful meteorite hunter.

Once a fireball has gone out, it continues to travel in what is known as *dark flight*. Atmospheric braking has slowed down the incoming material from its original entry velocity, and surviving fragments are thought to hit the Earth at between 200 and 300 miles per hour. Typically, the smallest pieces fall first, while the greater mass and inertia of the larger pieces carry them a greater distance. In a textbook strewnfield, we would find many small pieces at the "small end," less abundant but larger pieces in the middle, and a few very large masses at the "big end." If a fall zone is mapped and all the finds logged, it is often possible to draw a lazy circle around the fall zone and this is known as the strewnfield ellipse. Although it is a commonly used term in meteoritics, in my experience the distribution of fragments is usually more akin to the shape of an arrowhead.

If you have a rough idea of the boundaries of an existing strewnfield, you can plan where best to hunt. It is usually easier to find pieces at the small end, because there are likely to be more of them. However, some hunters prefer to gamble in the hopes of finding one large mass towards the big end, and larger masses are easier to see if they are on the surface, and easier to detect if they are buried. Bear in mind that the distribution of pieces based on size is only a model and there are always exceptions and variations. It is possible or even likely that a few small pieces will be found near the large end, and some medium-sized fragments will have fallen closer to the small end. By noting the size and location of all finds, you can begin to build a map of the strewnfield.

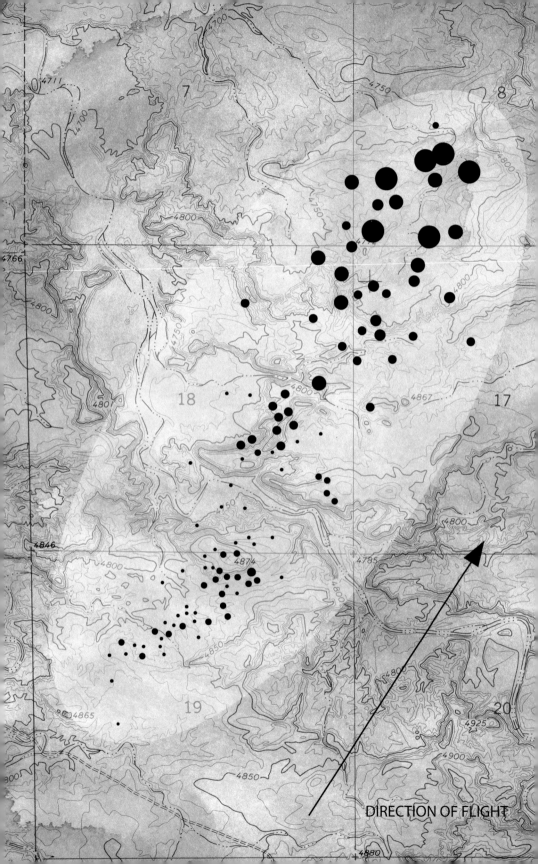

DIRECTION OF FLIGHT

Some strewnfields are quite small, and some are vast. You can walk from the smallest crater at Henbury, Australia, to the largest in about ten minutes, while the Gibeon strewnfield in Namibia covers hundreds of square miles. The size of a strewnfield is often related to the angle of entry taken by an incoming meteoroid. A steep angle of entry (close to vertical) will result in most or all fragments falling in a relatively small zone, while a long shallow angle (closer to horizontal) will give the meteoroid more time to fragment, all the while scattering material along its flight path.

The success I had while hunting the Park Forest fall (May 29, 2003, Illinois) is an example of how understanding the dynamics of a strewnfield helped recover multiple meteorites. Several large masses were seen to hit the roofs of houses in the Chicago suburb of Park Forest. My hunting team assumed these were the largest stones that had fallen, and we also knew the approximate angle of flight taken by the incoming meteoroid. By following the flight path upstream (away from the big end and toward the origin point), we increased our chances of finding other meteorites that were smaller than the house smashers, and which would have fallen a few seconds earlier.

After locating several mid-sized stones, we traveled further upstream and, as we did, the meteorites we found became smaller and smaller, until I noticed a 0.2-gram (0.007 of an ounce) specimen in a parking lot, many miles from the big end of the strewnfield. We chose to call that point the boundary of the small end of the strewnfield, as we probably would not be able to locate any smaller fragments.

In the following scenario, I take a team to an imaginary strewnfield in which I believe numerous meteorites have fallen. A fireball was seen over the fictitious town of Smithsburg and I receive a report that a farmer found a single meteorite of 100 grams (3.5 ounces) on his property. I assume that the 100-gram stone—being of modest size—is likely near the middle of the fall zone. After speaking to eyewitnesses, I get a good idea of the direction of the fireball. I travel upstream, against the flight path, towards the small end of the strewnfield. I find a 50-gram stone, and two hours later a 20-gram stone, so I know I am still within the strewnfield and continuing to move towards the small end. After another hour, I find a 5-gram stone and, after that, nothing, meaning I have likely moved out of the small end and entered an area where no meteorites fell. At that point I may backtrack and travel towards the big end, where I will hope to find fewer but larger masses.

If I mark all of my finds on a map and draw a line from the smallest to the largest, I can estimate with some accuracy, the direction of travel of the incoming meteoroid. By hunting along that line, and on either side of it, I maximize my chances of finding additional pieces.

[left] Artist's impression of a typical strewnfield ellipse and fall distribution. The black dots show where meteorites fell and also represent their varying sizes. Note how the average size increases as you follow the direction of flight towards the "big end" of the strewnfield.

FIREBALL'S DIRECTION OF FLIGHT

TEAM TWO
Team Two focuses on the middle of the fall zone, perhaps using a larger two-person PI detector, searching for mid-sized targets.

"SMALL END"
OF FALL ZONE

TEAM ONE
Team One hunts the strewnfield's small end by eye or with hand-held detectors. We expect meteorites here to be smaller in size, but greater in number.

"BIG END"
OF FALL ZONE

TEAM THREE
Team Three scouts with an off-road vehicle. We expect one or more larger meteorites to have fallen in the big end of the zone.

BASE CAMP
Make camp in the middle of the strewnfield. From then on, whatever you are doing, you are doing it in the fall zone. Even a casual after-dinner stroll could result in a new meteorite find! This also maximizes your productive time in the hunting zone.

TACTICAL OVERVIEW OF STREWNFIELD OPERATIONS

 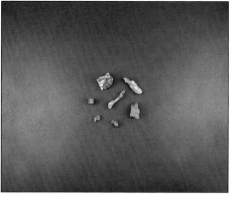

[above] What are the odds? During a hunt at Glorieta Mountain, New Mexico, I bagged every target as a demonstration. I was hunting a known strewnfield where many meteorites have been found in the past. I had hunted there before, was familiar with the terrain, had permission from landowners, and was using a detector I knew to be good at finding the type of meteorites I was looking for (pallasites). I had everything going for me, and yet I still had to excavate *many* pieces of trash for each meteorite. This is why the successful hunter must stay positive and dig every target. [below] Meteorites can fall anywhere and hunting conditions are often far from ideal. My friends Rob Reisener and Sonny Clary accompanied me on a harrowing expedition into the marshy woodlands of Alabama during a sweltering summer. We knew meteorites were there, but thick vegetation made hunting extremely difficult, even hazardous, as multiple species of venomous snakes are common in the area and poison ivy is abundant. We spent days wading through swamps, wearing snake boots, and had to stay constantly hydrated due to heat and humidity.

The illustration on pages 56 and 57 demonstrates how the team might use this information to conduct a thorough, ongoing hunt of the imaginary Smithsburg strewnfield. We now know the direction of flight and have already found several specimens. I set up base camp near the middle of the strewnfield, where we can expect to find a modest number of medium-sized meteorites. We are now based *inside* the fall zone, so even a post-dinner stroll could produce a meteorite! Part of my team hunts the small end on foot, by eye, and with detectors. We expect to find larger numbers of smaller meteorites there. Two team members hunt the middle of the zone using a larger pulse indication (PI) detector (see page 104). This tactic will be most useful in an iron or stony-iron strewnfield as larger PI units are particularly effective with big, iron-rich targets. Finally, two team members scout the big end, where one or more very large meteorites may have fallen. They cover ground fast in an off-road vehicle, hoping to spot a sizeable target on the surface.

Every strewnfield is different and you will need to employ a variety of tactics on each hunt, but understanding a strewnfield's approximate size and direction will greatly improve your chances of finding meteorites within it.

[above] Meteorites are where you find them. They can be discovered in the strangest (or most ordinary) of places. I found this excellent 21.5-gram fusion-crusted whole stone sitting in a parking lot in a Chicago suburb a few days after the Park Forest meteorite fall of March 26, 2003. I put my wristwatch on the rain-soaked pavement for scale and took my *in-situ* photograph before bagging and recording the find.

The author and Steve Arnold with the 101-kg (223-lb) Admire pallasite they discovered while filming *Meteorite Men* Season Two, in Kansas. The strewnfield tactics discussed in the preceding chapter were employed to make this spectacular find.

METEORITE CRATERS AND IMPACT PITS

Craters are formed when large meteorites traveling with sufficient velocity hit the Earth, resulting in an explosive event. Most meteorites do not form craters, either because they were not large enough or were not traveling quickly enough. Small meteorites often come to rest on the surface of the ground without even making an indentation. Meteorites that land in soft ground sometimes punch a hole into the soil and become entirely hidden; I witnessed this phenomenon with both the Park Forest and the Ash Creek (February 15, 2009, West, Texas) falls. Larger meteorites, especially if they land in sand or dry soil, may remain where they fell, sitting in a shallow, concave indentation known as an impact pit. I have seen very distinctive impact pits—some almost the size of a child's wading pool—in the Imilac and Vaca Muerta strewnfields in Chile.

If you look at the surface of the Moon through a telescope, you will notice that it is covered with impact craters. Our planet has also been pummeled by meteorites—large and small—for billions of years, but the protective curtain of our atmosphere both retards and ablates potential meteorites, meaning less material makes it to the ground. The air that we breathe slows down incoming meteoroids and reduces their mass. Our planet is also a dynamic entity with moving tectonic plates, oceans, wind, and rain; the Moon is not. The geologic processes at work on the Earth continually change the shape of the landscape, meaning very old

[left] Hidden deep in Canadian woods, the Whitecourt Crater in Alberta is only about 1,100 years old and is a protected site. [above] The majestic 700,000-year-old Monturaqui Crater in northern Chile.

meteorite craters will be eroded over time, and this is well demonstrated by some ancient impact structures such as Vredefort (South Africa) and the Alamo Breccia (Nevada). As we have already discussed, most meteorites are rich in iron and will likely decay over the millennia in our oxygen-rich, moist atmosphere. Ancient meteorite craters, therefore, should not be expected to produce meteorites, which may have completely decomposed. The remote Monturaqui Crater in Chile's northern Atacama Desert is estimated to be approximately 700,000 years old and is an good example of what happens to crater-forming iron meteorites over time. While *impactites*— terrestrial rocks that have been melted or altered by the tremendous heat and pressure of a large meteorite impact—are relatively abundant and well-preserved around the crater, all that remains of the original impactor is weathered fragments, most of which are less than 2 grams in weight.

There are fewer than 200 positively identified separate meteorite crater sites worldwide (the Sikhote-Alin strewnfield in Siberia comprises about 100 distinct craters, but is only listed as one site). Most of them are very old, and less than 20 have produced actual meteorite specimens. The Earth Impact Database, managed by the Planetary and Space Science Centre (PASSC) at the University of New Brunswick, is an excellent resource; it provides a list of all known craters and crater fields.

[left] Meteor Crater in northern Arizona is regarded as the best-preserved large meteorite impact site on Earth, and is between 25,000 and 50,000 years old. The iron meteorites found around the crater are named Canyon Diablo after a nearby geological feature. [top] The author standing inside an impact pit formed by a large piece of the Imilac meteorite, Atacama Desert, Chile. [above] The largest of 15 meteorite craters at the Henbury Crater Preserve in Australia's Northern Territories. The impact is estimated to have occurred about 5,000 years ago and the event was almost certainly witnessed by indigenous people.

[top] Sometimes extreme measures are required to reach the most inaccessible sites. During a 1999 expedition to Siberia's Popigai Crater, led by Professor Roy Gallant, the only way in or out was by a cargo helicopter that landed us *inside* the crater. The cliff faces behind us are composed of impactites and were once part of the floor of the ancient astrobleme. [above] The Rassokha River flows though Popigai. During our nine days inside the crater, we traveled from one site to another using inflatable rafts.

The first significant impact structure to be widely studied was the famous, and erroneously named, Meteor Crater (craters are formed by meteorites, not meteors) in northern Arizona. Daniel Moreau Barringer, a mining engineer and entrepreneur, was convinced that a gigantic meteorite lay buried beneath the crater floor. During the early 1900s, he spent several years and a substantial fortune drilling and trying to locate the hidden mass. We now know that meteorites are not found buried at the bottom of large craters, except for some small fragments that may have fallen back inside after the event. Meteorite craters are formed by an impact and explosion of immense proportions. As a result, much of the meteorite is destroyed and any pieces that are not vaporized are thrown outside of the crater. In some instances, ejected fragments have been found miles from the actual point of impact. So, if you are searching for meteorites at a known crater site, the hunt should begin at the rim and move outwards with the help of metal detectors.

Many of the world's most famous impact sites, such as Meteor Crater, Wolf Creek (Australia), and Odessa (Texas) are protected, and meteorite hunting is not allowed. One of the things that drew me to the Monturaqui Crater, and prompted a second complicated expedition to the hostile Atacama Desert in order to see it, was the fact that it is remote, undisturbed, and access is unrestricted. I had the unforgettable experience of camping overnight on the floor of the actual crater—something that could be accomplished at only a handful of sites worldwide. When driving down to the crater floor with our camping equipment, my team's vehicles were careful to follow existing dirt tracks so as not to damage the crater walls.

People frequently contact me, certain that they have discovered a new meteorite crater. New discoveries are rare—perhaps one new meteorite crater comes to light every year or so. Impact specialists actively search for new craters using satellite imaging and mapping software. Even with this advanced technology, the chances of finding a new crater are slim, but it does happen. In 2007, a new impact site was discovered in northern Alberta in Canada, and it is now known as the Whitecourt Crater. Deep in the woods, the site had been known for generations by woodsmen and hunters and was regarded locally as a strange anomaly. Some enthusiasts had visited the site with metal detectors, after a brief search, began finding rusty, angular, metallic fragments. Those pieces were taken to the University of Alberta and positively identified as type IIIAB iron meteorites. In the fall of 2009, I was lucky enough to be one of the very first people to hunt at Whitecourt. My team received express permission from the university to search there, and we found a number of excellent pieces. Whitecourt, like many other craters, is a national preserve, and there is a $25,000 fine for hunting in the restricted area. Despite the serious consequences, illegal meteorite poaching continues at the site. The data associated with stolen pieces are now lost forever. As a result, Canada's University of Alberta in Edmonton asked Steve Arnold and me to return to Whitecourt Crater in 2011 and use our expertise to recover as many meteorite fragments as possible for them before they were lost to illegal poaching. We were allowed into the protected zone that immediately surrounds the crater and found hundreds of pieces. Meteorites were so abundant near the crater that, in some cases, it was not possible to walk two feet without getting a target! It was an amazing and likely never-to-be-repeated experience. We precisely recorded the depth, orientation, and soil type for every find and this irreplaceable information was provided to Dr. Chris Herd, who went on to produce a magnificent three-dimensional map of the crater and surrounding area, showing the dispersal of iron fragments. It is likely the most detailed map of its kind. Many other meteorite hunters also provided find data to Dr. Herd and this is an outstanding example of how academia and commercial interests can and do work together for the benefit of science.

There are many natural and man-made features that have been mistaken for meteorite craters, and these include bomb craters, sink holes, stock tanks, dried-up watering holes and ponds, and even buffalo wallows.

[above] The picturesque town of Nördlingen in southern Germany is situated within the vast Nördlinger Ries Crater, formed approximately 14 million years ago by a giant meteorite. The blue line clearly visible at the horizon is the actual rim of the crater. [right] This 34-kg (75-lb) iron meteorite took three entire days to excavate from beside one of Morasko, Poland's 5000-year-old craters. At the time, it was the second-largest meteorite ever found in Poland, and also the deepest at 2 meters (6 feet). The area was flooded and littered with military ordnance and relics. The excavation was dangerous and extremely difficult, and the meteorite was only recovered because my team remained relentless and determined.

If you think you have discovered a new meteorite crater, start by examining historical records of the area. Was mining carried out at the site? Was it once a farm or military test range? If the answer to one of these questions is yes, then any crater-like formations may have been caused by earlier human activities.

If it is the real thing, a search with metal detectors around the rim of the feature may turn up meteorite fragments. If there are no meteorite fragments to be found, the positive identification of an impact site can be complex. Verification requires the expertise of impact specialists who may search for shocked quartz, the presence of the element iridium (rare on Earth but more abundant in meteorites), and impactites. Some sites that appear to be ancient craters, such as the Upheaval Dome in Utah, are still a source of debate among academics, so there is not always an easy answer to be found regarding the origin of strange circular depressions in the ground.

Very large impact sites are sometimes called *astroblemes* (star wounds). The Popigai Crater in northern Siberia is one such site. Its great age of 35.7 million years and phenomenal size—100 kilometers (62.5 miles) in diameter—make it one of the five largest known astroblemes on earth. I had the great privilege of joining the very first international team to visit Popigai on a 1999 expedition led by the great astronomer, author, and adventurer Professor Roy Gallant. He chronicled our three-week expedition in his book *Meteorite Hunter*. Even though any meteorites that survived the cataclysmic Popigai event had long since vanished, it was one of the most exciting adventures of my career, and I returned to the United States with a marvelous collection of impactites. Some of those specimens contain microdiamonds formed by the intense heat and pressure of that ancient impact.

Meteorite craters are the point at which asteroids and our planet intersect, with sometimes apocalyptic results. In addition to being promising sites for meteorite hunters, they are also places of extraordinary beauty and wonder. Well-preserved meteorite craters are rare and important historic sites and should be treated with respect. The passage of tourists and cattle have caused erosion to the walls of the Henbury Craters in Australia, and although visitors are welcome to walk around them, special permission is required to venture down inside.

The days I spent exploring craters at Henbury in Australia, Whitecourt in Canada, Morasko in Poland, and many others, are among the most memorable times of my life. Even more so, were overnight sojourns within the magnificent Monturaqui Crater in Chile, Nördlinger Ries in Germany, and the massive Popigai Crater in Siberia.

Even if you cannot get permission to hunt at a protected crater site, consider giving it a visit. The grandeur of these footprints of cosmic devastation are both inspiring and humbling—a reminder of how vulnerable our little planet really is.

THE IMPORTANCE OF RESEARCH

Another question I am frequently asked is: "How do you know where to look for meteorites?" If I am chasing a witnessed fireball in an attempt to locate freshly-fallen rocks, then I usually have a fairly good idea of where to begin the hunt. But most of my work takes place at sites where meteorites have been found before. If numerous meteorites fell at a known spot, it is possible or even likely that not all of them have been recovered. The great meteorite hunter and researcher Harvey Harlow Nininger was fond of saying that a strewnfield is never fully hunted out. I have proved him right time and again. Heavily-hunted and well-known strewnfields such as Brenham (Kansas), Vaca Muerta (Chile), Morasko (Poland), Muonionalusta (Sweden), and others, have delivered *major* finds for me and my team even though I was well aware that many people had hunted those areas before me.

There are several reasons why we may be able to return to sites that have already been thoroughly searched, yet still be successful. One factor is that some strewnfields are very large, covering ten, twenty, one hundred square miles or more. It is virtually impossible to carefully search every square foot of a strewnfield that could be the size of hundreds of football fields, so a thorough, meticulous search will often produce meteorites that others have missed. Other considerations are improvements in equipment and in your own abilities. I have, many times, visited well-documented strewnfields and found new material because I was using better detectors or because my skill and knowledge as a hunter had increased over time.

Research becomes one of the most important tools in the meteorite hunter's arsenal. Meteorites have fallen over the entire surface of our planet and—odds are—one probably landed somewhere near you. Read books about meteorites, look in newspaper archives for stories about historic witnessed falls, sift through scientific papers and see if you can find a clue that will help you know where to begin your hunt.

The Meteoritical Bulletin Database is an excellent online resource, as it lists all officially classified meteorite falls and finds, many of them with coordinates. Bear in mind that not all published coordinates are precise. Sometimes only an approximate find location is given—such as the nearest town—and there have been cases where meteorite finders have deliberately provided inaccurate information in order to prevent others from hunting at "their" sites. Other find locations are simply not known. An example is the Turtle River iron meteorite from Minnesota. One mass of 22.39 kg (49 lbs) was reportedly plowed up by a farmer in Beltrami County during the 1950s, but it was not until 1968 that the iron was identified as an authentic meteorite by Glenn Huss of the American Meteorite Laboratory. During the intervening years, details of the exact find location were forgotten, and it remains a mystery to this day. There are many such stories, and many "lost" meteorites waiting to be rediscovered.

Sometimes I carry out my own research, and sometimes I hire a specialist to assist me. My staff researcher is an experienced meteorite collector, writer, and an expert on vintage maps, making her a perfect addition to my team. Research is a skill like anything else, so when I ran into problems planning an expedition to the Henbury Crater in Australia, I enlisted her help. After examining obscure papers, maps, and documents in various archives, my researcher was able to provide me with valuable clues about old find locations that led to some significant meteorite discoveries during that trip.

The more time you spend planning and researching, the better your chances of finding something when you arrive at your chosen hunting ground (see Chapter 17 for more about preparing for an expedition).

[top] The Park Forest meteorite fall of 2003 occurred over a major urban area (greater Chicago). It was vital to ensure we only hunted on land for which we had clear access and permission. [above] This meteorite find weighed well over 124 kg (273 lbs) and had to be removed from the ground with a backhoe. This type of large-scale operation requires special permission and cooperation from landowners.

OWNERSHIP, LANDOWNERS, AND PERMISSION TO HUNT

The ownership of meteorites is a potentially complicated issue, and something the would-be meteorite hunter must research before commencing a hunting trip. In the United States, meteorites found on private land typically belong to the landowner. In other words, if a meteorite fell in my neighbor's yard and I found it, the rock would still belong to him. Meteorites recovered on federal land belong to the Smithsonian Institution and should be turned over for study. The Bureau of Land Management (BLM) has sensible regulations in place and allows "casual" collection of meteorites from the surface. Commercial collecting is also permitted, but a permit is required.

"Casually collected" meteorites from BLM land are for personal use only and cannot be sold, making such locations attractive for the collector, but not for the meteorite hunter who makes a living from finding and selling space rocks. Local BLM officers will be able to advise you on the specifics of areas they oversee, or refer to the BLM website.

State laws vary; check with appropriate authorities to determine if it is legal to hunt in your target area.

Most national monuments and national parks prohibit the removal of *any* material at all—meteorites, plants, rocks, even sand—and there are serious penalties for those who are foolish enough to ignore federal regulations. The use of metal detectors is illegal in most federal reserves and hefty fines and even jail time can be imposed on anyone caught poaching.

In some cases, such as inside the Lake Mead National Recreation Area, which encompasses part of the Gold Basin strewnfield, my team and I received express permission from the National Park Service to hunt in an area which is a restricted federal reserve. In order to do so, we had to enlist an academic sponsor (in this case the Oscar E. Monnig Meteorite Collection at TCU, Fort Worth), and arrange for an experienced Park Ranger to accompany my team on the hunt. Every find was carefully documented and turned over to the Park Service, which then presented all of our meteorites from that expedition to the Monnig Collection on long-term loan. We knew, going in, that we would not be able to keep a single meteorite, but it was worth it for the experience of hunting in an undisturbed area.

Due to the complexity of obtaining permission to hunt on some federal and state land, I often prefer to work with private landowners. After I have determined who owns the land on which I am interested in hunting, a meeting is arranged to ask for permission to work on that property. Some landowners are very supportive and interested in my work. Generous property owners have sometimes allowed me not only to hunt on their land, but also to keep everything I find. In most cases, I make a deal with the landowner and turn over a percentage of all finds, either in the form of money or material. In other cases, I may offer to pay a flat fee to hunt for a set period of time.

There are no set guidelines or fixed percentages for this type of operation, as each site is different, and each meteorite find is unique. Be respectful to landowners and be straightforward with them. Gaining access to someone's property is a privilege, not a right. While I have generally been welcomed by property owners, there have also been cases of would-be meteorite hunters getting chased off private land with a shotgun. Meteorites often fall in rural areas, and sometimes people choose to live in remote areas for a reason; they do not want to be bothered by others. If a landowner does not want you on his or her property, move on. Badgering property owners gives meteorite hunters a bad name and can get you into trouble. Remember that trespassing and removing material from someone's land without permission are crimes for which you can be prosecuted.

[above] The author with a new find: A lovely fusion-crusted stone meteorite from the Buzzard Coulee fall. This specimen was lying on the surface and was recovered using just a simple, hand-made magnet cane.

Some meteorite hunters have set an unfortunate precedent in which they offer to give up 50% of all finds to their host. While this may be viable in certain cases, a 50/50 split is not always realistic or fair. I may spend months, even years, working at a particular site. An extended search will likely involve me and my team bringing in sophisticated, heavy equipment, paying for hotel bills, gasoline, supplies, and other operating expenses. If one or more finds are made, we then have to excavate and invest more time in identifying, preparing, and possibly selling the recovered material. Although it is true that the landowner is the legal owner of meteorites on his property, our expertise and expenditure of time, money, and effort are worth a great deal to the partnership between owner and hunter. And, most landowners, simply do not have the time or knowledge to recover meteorites, even when they are lying on their own property.

In April of 2009, I journeyed to western Saskatchewan, Canada, with my great friend and sometime hunting partner, Lisa Marie Morrison (see photo on page 86). We were hoping to find pieces of the Buzzard Coulee stone meteorite which had fallen over many square miles of rolling farmland, following a spectacular fireball in November of the previous year. One of our colleagues had already provided us with valuable local intelligence, so our first mission was to meet with the owner of our prime hunting location.

We quickly came to an arrangement with him. We were hunting on foot, armed only with magnet canes, and did not require the assistance of heavy equipment so, in this case, we happily agreed to a 50/50 split. The owner was trusting and gentlemanly, and granted us full access to his extensive property without any supervision.

During a thrilling multi-day hunt, we found over 100 fresh stone meteorites. At the end of the expedition, Lisa and I returned to the landowner's office and showed him all of our finds. He graciously allowed us to choose which pieces we wanted to keep for ourselves.

Our Buzzard Coulee hunt was the perfect example of how meteorite hunting can be a constructive experience for all parties involved. Lisa and I were able to conduct a thorough search with full permission; we found numerous fine pieces, some of which were sold and some kept for personal collections. In return, the landowner received a significant quantity of valuable meteorites, which he sold for additional income. It was a strange experience when, much later, a part-time meteorite dealer contacted me by email and offered to sell me stones that I, myself, had found years earlier (he had purchased them from the landowner).

The Buzzard Coulee hunt was a happy and productive partnership in which both landowner and hunting team benefitted — as did science, actually, because one of our finds was very significant and later went to an important museum collection, where it remains to this day.

SOME EXAMPLES OF INTERNATIONAL REGULATIONS

The Buzzard expedition illustrated another important point: Even though we were extremely successful and found a large number of stones, we did not take any of them home with us at the end of the trip.

Meteorites found in Canada cannot leave the country without an official export permit. This regulation ensures that Canadian academics have the opportunity—if they wish—to purchase, at fair market value, finds made in Canada, thereby ensuring that important meteorites remain in the country for study. Before we left for home, we mailed all of our meteorites to a colleague who lives in Canada. We went home successful, but—at least temporarily—empty-handed. In the case of the Buzzard Coulee fall, a number of fine specimens had already been made available to academia for research purposes, so the Canadian authorities eventually released our finds. When our specimens arrived in the United States, it was an exciting day. We got to see our finds again, happy in the knowledge that we followed an established and sensible protocol and were now in possession of legally exported meteorites.

Regulations in Australia are different: all meteorite finds belong to the Commonwealth and cannot be removed from the country without written approval. Export permits are sometimes granted but, again, this takes time and must be done through proper channels. While hunting in Australia at the famous Henbury and Mundrabilla sites in 2010, I found many meteorites including several exceptional larger specimens. It was quite heartbreaking to leave them behind in Australia, but I was eventually granted export permits and—some months later—my finds made their way safely, and legally, to the United States where they found a happy home in my personal collection.

Argentina, home of the massive Campo del Cielo strewnfield, no longer allows the exportation of any meteorites; neither does Namibia, the African nation which encompasses the great Gibeon strewnfield. If you are planning to search for meteorites overseas, be very sure to check legalities first. Winding up in a foreign prison would not be a pleasant end to an expedition.

In general, commercial and academic interests work together well for the benefit of science and the community. We support and encourage this form of mutually beneficial cooperation, but bad behavior by a few has resulted in some countries banning meteorite recovery entirely, and unethical hunters have been arrested and detained for illegal meteorite collecting. Do not be one of those selfish few who cast a bad light on the good work done by the majority of hunters and enthusiasts.

[right] Hard, flat, empty, dry surfaces like this expanse of the Western Sahara are ideal locations for meteorite hunting. The wilderness may seem as if it's beyond the reach of the law, but all land is owned by somebody—or some government. Do your homework before embarking on an expedition and make sure it is legal to search for meteorites where you are going.

HUNTING STRATEGIES: HISTORIC METEORITES AND KNOWN STREWNFIELDS

Some meteorite hunters enjoy the excitement of a fresh fireball chase. My friend Sonny Clary prefers the challenge and solitude of long-range desert hunts for cold finds. I love research, and history, and the history of meteorites; for me, there is nothing more satisfying than visiting classic locations such as Odessa (Texas), Holbrook (Arizona), or Mundrabilla (Australia) and—with a lot of dedication and a bit of luck—proving, once again, that the old strewnfields are never really hunted out.

The extraordinary success enjoyed by Steve Arnold at the Brenham strewnfield should be a reminder to not always believe what you are told by meteorite experts. Meteorites were first found at the site in the 1880s. Harvey Nininger recovered hundreds of pounds during his 1933 expedition, and H.O. Stockwell found a mass weighing 454 kg (1,000 lbs) in 1949. Since then, almost every serious meteorite hunter in the country has been over the site; if you asked anyone about Brenham, he or she would say: "It's all hunted out. Don't waste your time there." Steve did not agree.

In 2005, Steve invited me to the strewnfield to experiment with a new hunting strategy. We pulled hundreds of pounds of Brenhams out of the ground, including the largest ever found, which was discovered by Steve and which weighs a staggering 650 kg (1,430 lbs).

There are many strewnfields in this country and overseas where there are still meteorites in the ground. This is not my opinion; it is a fact. Gold Basin (Arizona) is still producing meteorites and it was first discovered in 1995. Since then, scores of meteorite enthusiasts have been to the site, some of them many times. A few gold prospectors camped there for months, and found literally hundreds of pieces. The Gold Basin strewnfield is very well known, and relatively easy to get to. There are still meteorites to be found, which gives you an idea of the tremendous amount of material that must have fallen there about 20,000 years ago.

I once received a letter from a man who had enthusiastically watched my television shows and decided to take his son hunting at one of the sites featured. It was their first hunt, but on just the second day they made a find. It so happened that the gentleman lived in the Washington, D.C. area. Later that year, when I was a guest speaker in D.C., he brought their find to show me. Not only was it a real meteorite, but it was a lovely piece. It was the first meteorite they had ever recovered. This story demonstrates that it *is* possible to find meteorites right out of the gate.

I have personally found meteorites in at least twenty different historic

[left] Excavating a complete 870-gram stone meteorite in the Gold Basin strewnfield. While the exposed surfaces had weathered considerably, fusion crust and regmaglypts were present on the buried sections. It turned out to be the best-preserved fusion crust we had ever seen on a Gold Basin specimen.

The Morasko preserve near Posnan, Poland encompasses several craters and is a protected zone. Some of the craters have filled with water and are now connected by scenic forest paths. It is one of the most tranquil and beautiful scientific locations I have ever visited. After receiving special permission to conduct a search with modern detectors, my team found a massive 75-lb meteorite at this site that everyone told us was "hunted out."

strewnfields that had already been heavily hunted and which were thought to warrant no further search time. I was successful because I put in the time, used good equipment, tried to think outside the box, and did my research.

Meteorites can fall anywhere. Chances are there is an old strewnfield in your home state or county, maybe even close to your home. The United States is rich in documented meteorite falls. In 1807, an H4 chondrite fell near Weston, Connecticut. Over 150 kg (330 lbs) of material was recovered. There are probably more out there. More than 220 kg (484 lbs) of stones have been collected from the 1912 fall near Holbrook, Arizona. Norton County (Kansas) is a rare aubrite meteorite and a staggering 1.1 metric tons have been collected since the fall in 1948. These are just a few examples.

A good way to get started is to compile a list of meteorite falls and finds in your home state. Do some research on that type of meteorite: Is it a stone or an iron? How much is the meteorite likely to have deteriorated in the intervening years since its initial discovery? Are there any scientific

papers or newspaper articles available that you can study?

Hunting in old strewnfields can be difficult for several reasons: Other people know about the site, so the easy-to-find pieces have probably already been picked up; over time, meteorites will become hidden under leaves, grass, or soil and, in some cases, new housing developments obliterate old fall zones; meteorites will oxidize and eventually decay in moist environments. These are obstacles that all meteorite hunters face but, as my *Meteorite Men* co-host Steve Arnold is fond of saying: "If it was easy, everyone would be doing it."

You may not find anything on your first hunt, or your first ten hunts, but if you spend sufficient time exploring old strewnfields, you will begin to hone your skills. Your map reading abilities will improve; you will become more familiar with your GPS, metal detector, and digging tools; you will gain valuable experience in talking to landowners and initiating your own research.

Meteorites are most definitely out there in the world; it is just a question of figuring out exactly where they are hiding.

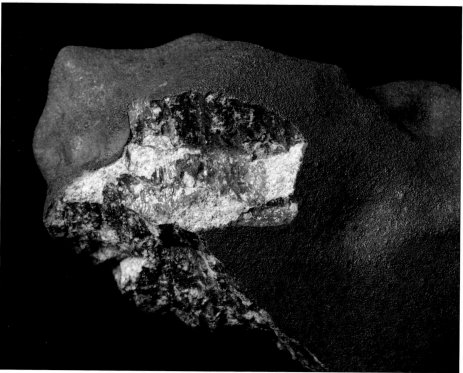

[top] These complete, fusion-crusted Chelyabinsk stone meteorites show the remarkable diversity in size of fallen specimens, which here range from 0.2 to 282.4 grams. It is, in a sense, a miniature strewnfield. Many small specimens like these were collected by children as they lay, untouched, atop freshly-fallen snow. [above] Detail of one of the bigger Chelyabinsk stones recovered from what was the largest single recorded meteorite event since Sikhote-Alin (1947). This stone broke during flight, or upon impact, revealing a complex mottled grey and white (brecciated) interior.

HUNTING STRATEGIES: FIREBALL CHASING

A few times each year a large fireball is seen in the skies over our planet. The term *bolide* is often used to describe a fireball that is seen to break up, or explode, during flight. Some fireballs are old satellites or rocket fuel tanks burning up, but the most impressive fireballs are caused by cosmic debris entering our atmosphere. Some fireballs are completely consumed; others fragment and send meteorite pieces raining down upon the Earth. When such an event occurs, enthusiasts may race to the scene, try to determine where pieces landed, and recover them if possible. This exciting and often challenging type of meteorite hunting is known as fireball chasing.

EYEWITNESS REPORTS

I often commence a new fireball chase by interviewing eyewitnesses. In such cases it is vital to take into account the ways in which untrained observers may react to the shock and surprise of seeing such an event.

Due to their great brightness, large meteors and fireballs often create a remarkable optical illusion in which it appears that they have hit the ground somewhere nearby, especially if they are observed at night. The glowing fireballs we see in the sky are caused by atmospheric resistance and friction, but meteors stop ablating while they are at least seven miles high. If you are lucky enough to witness a bright fireball, and it begins dark flight while approaching you or directly overhead, it is possible that meteorites will land nearby. When a fireball apparently lands in the vicinity, what we are actually seeing is it arcing away over the horizon, still high up in the atmosphere. Due to the curvature of the Earth, the fireball may seem to hit the ground, but has in fact moved out of our field of view and gone beyond the horizon. Because of their extreme brightness, fireballs can appear—to our human eyes—to be much closer than they really are. It is something I, myself, have been fortunate enough to witness a couple of times, which can be frustrating because it does look as if meteorites landed "just over there." If anything made it to the ground, however, it probably landed hundreds of miles away.

Such optical illusions can make eyewitness accounts of fireballs unreliable. Most fireball events last for only a few seconds, and most witnesses are not trained astronomical observers. Sometimes interviewees will insist that the fireball they saw was much closer than it possibly could have been. In 2009, I spoke with a number of people in Tucson who had excellent views of a June 23 fireball which caused a small number of meteorites to fall near the Whetstone Mountains in southern Arizona. One eyewitness was walking to his vehicle in a parking lot when the fireball streaked by. He insisted it was so close that he could feel heat on his face! This was clearly impossible, as the fireball was still many miles up at the time.

When interviewing witnesses who give confusing or clearly inaccurate reports, the best course of action is to be gracious, thank them for their time, and move on. There is no point standing in a parking lot arguing the laws of physics with someone who *knows* what he saw.

SONIC BOOMS

By collecting reliable eyewitness reports, I can begin to plot a course for the fireball. Reports from people who also heard sonic booms or other associated sounds are the most valuable. When a body such as a jet aircraft or a meteoroid travels through the air faster than the speed of sound, a sonic boom is created. The explosion of a meteoroid during flight can also generate significant sound waves. A bright fireball can sometimes be seen from hundreds of miles away, especially at night. Sound waves do not travel as far, and they also travel much more slowly than light. Spectators who heard sonic booms, in addition to seeing the fireball are, therefore, usually within, or close to, the flight path. While investigating the Ash Creek fireball in Texas, I visited one landowner who showed me a window that had been cracked by the sonic boom. His house was directly under the line of flight.

VIDEO SURVEILLANCE FOOTAGE: THE MOST RELIABLE EYEWITNESS

Our modern world is full of video cameras: security cameras outside of private homes, banks, and warehouses; small units mounted on police cars, and so on. Fireballs do not last for long, so the chances of an individual happening to be filming with a smart phone or video camera during those few seconds are pretty slim, but it has happened. The Peekskill event of 1992 is an excellent example. Its spectacular flight was captured by several different individuals who were filming their kids in high school football games when the fireball rocketed overhead.

Video surveillance footage is highly prized by meteorite hunters. It is typically more reliable than eyewitness accounts, and it can be watched over and over again in an attempt to determine velocity and angle of flight. If video footage can be collected from more than one camera, and those cameras were pointed at different angles, we can sometimes calculate—with some degree of accuracy—where meteorites might have fallen.

[left] When it works, it really works! On the first day of my first expedition to the Buzzard Coulee, Canada strewnfield, my friend and hunting partner, Lisa Marie Morrison, asked where I thought we should start searching. I knew the direction of flight of the meteorite-forming fireball (it had gone directly over our heads) and I also knew where a few pieces had already been found, so I used the strategy described on page 55 to select our initial hunt site. We got out of the car, braced ourselves against the freezing late-winter wind, and hiked up a steep scarp. It wasn't five minutes until Lisa shouted: "Is this one?" It was only her second meteorite hunt and she made her first find right out of the car. It isn't often that easy, but when it is, the excitement is indescribable.

DOPPLER RADAR

In recent years meteorite hunters have begun to appreciate the usefulness of Doppler radar, and how it can aid in tracking fireballs. Doppler is used in aviation, aerospace, and weather forecasting as it monitors objects in the sky such as aircraft and cloud banks. If a large incoming meteoroid breaks up at an altitude of, for example, eight miles, a debris cloud of fragments will begin to fall and may take several minutes to reach the ground. Doppler radar systems used for weather prediction employ a periodic circular sweep, and if that sweep is in the right place at the right time, it may produce an image of plummeting meteorite fragments. Doppler data was used successfully for the first time during the Ash Creek fireball hunt in 2009. Data from the National Weather Center in Oxnard, California gave searchers on the ground a good idea of where to look for meteoritic material. I have several times participated in hunts which used Doppler information to predict where meteorites might have fallen. Most of those hunts produced meteorite finds and working with Doppler images is one of the most promising technologies available to the meteorite hunter.

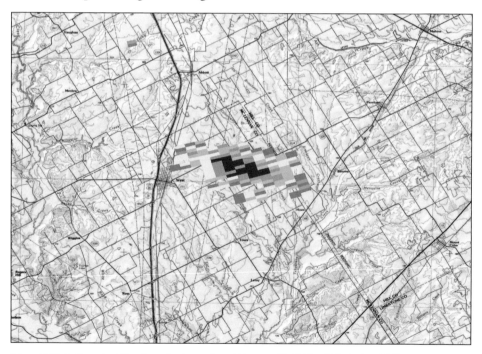

[above] This is the actual Doppler radar image from February 15, 2009 which depicted falling debris from the Ash Creek fireball. Pieces fell near West, Texas and Doppler data was used for the first time during that hunt (radar image courtesy of Robert Matson). [right] This complete fusion-crusted example of the Indian Butte stone meteorite lay on the desert surface near the town of Casa Grande, Arizona, from 1998, when it was part of a witnessed fireball, until it was discovered in 2012. The dark black section was above the surface, while the lighter grey portion was buried in the sand. Note how the buried section is actually more weathered and shows some rust due to moisture in the ground. This piece was found by eye, by an experienced meteorite hunter, using only a magnet cane.

BOOTS ON THE GROUND

Once my hunting team has narrowed the search area down to a manageable size, it is time to get boots on the ground. More than once, we have been out scouting a possible fall zone and have found a meteorite just lying in the road. If you consider how much asphalt there is in the world, driving all the roads in a suspected fall area allows you to cover a lot of ground quickly.

Much of the populated world is still covered by farmland and it seems that two out of every three fireball chases result in us getting to know some rural farmers. When we have arrived at the search area the most immediate matter at hand is getting permission to hunt (see Chapter 9).

Nearly every square foot of land in the United States is owned by someone, whether it be private, state, or federal. Hunting on private property without permission is unethical and illegal. Asking for permission from property owners is the right thing to do and can often add useful intelligence to the mix. If I am hunting within the fireball's path, it is likely that homeowners in the area heard or saw something that can help me with the search. Once in a while a local resident will amaze me by reporting that he heard something hit his roof—hard—shortly after the fireball, and such news can turn a chase into a successful recovery. Meteorites that have hit man-made objects, such as cars or buildings, are informally called "hammer stones" and are coveted by certain collectors.

When hunting in farmland, it is important to be respectful of the farmer's property and that can include livestock and crops. More often than not, that means walking on foot, with no equipment except for magnet canes.

If my team can make even one meteorite find, then the game is really

afoot. By plotting the location of that find in relation to the fireball's flight path, we can begin to map the strewnfield and determine where other pieces might have fallen (see Chapter 6).

THE REALITIES

An average strewnfield might encompass 15 square miles or more, and that may not seem like such a big area until you start trying to cover it by foot.

Freshly-fallen meteorites are highly sought after by researchers and collectors, and even one light rain will cause some meteorites to rust, thereby diminishing their scientific and financial value. There is always an urgency to recover pieces; bad weather might be expected, or farmers may be planting or harvesting crops. Tractors can easily bury small meteorites, causing them to be lost forever. You may find yourself competing in the field with others who are searching for space rocks — professionals, academics, amateurs, or curious locals — and the excitement of the hunt can bring out the worst in some. I have, unfortunately, witnessed instances where unscrupulous meteorite hunters have lied to landowners, bad-mouthed rival teams, or brazenly pretended to be scientists representing a university in order to gain access to private property! One part-time meteorite hunter promised landowners a share of everything he found, then sneaked out of town without giving the property owner a penny. Such antics give all meteorite hunters a bad name, and can do lasting and long-term damage.

Fossil collecting, a hobby once enjoyed by all who were interested, is now strictly regulated and controlled in the USA, with massive fines and penalties for those who break the law. Those laws were enacted after elitist interests argued that commercial collectors were damaging important sites. We do not want the same thing to happen to meteorite collecting, so act responsibly.

Fireball chasing is hard work. Statistically, the majority of meteorites that land are small, and you may spend a great deal of time hiking through rough ground, trying to spot tiny black rocks in tall grass, and wondering what ever possessed you to want to be a meteorite hunter in the first place. To make matters worse, sometimes there is just nothing there. For example, when searching for pieces of the Mifflin, Wisconsin, fireball I compared notes with other hunters. After averaging my colleagues' time in the field, the results were discouraging: One meteorite recovered for approximately every 65 man-hours of hunting time — and these were experienced hunters who knew exactly what to look for.

Many meteoroids burn up completely in the atmosphere and no meteoritic material survives to be found. The only way to know for sure is to look, and the payoff can be great. There are few things as exciting as picking up a pristine meteorite that — only hours or days earlier — was still part of the cosmos.

[top] An assortment of meteorwrongs found while hunting, including: Shrapnel from an artillery shell, Civil War bullets, riding tack, aircraft parts, .50-caliber machine gun cartridges, nails, bolts, and the cylinder from a Wild West revolver. [above] Persistence pays off. In 2009, I rushed to the Ash Creek (Texas) strewnfield a few days after the fireball of February 15. I found 13 meteorites in less than a week, while competing with other meteorite hunters. Seven months later, I returned and found this 36.8-gram meteorite in plain sight, in an area that had already been hunted by numerous other people.

HUNTING STRATEGIES: COLD FINDS, HOT DESERT HUNTING, AND DRY LAKE BEDS

When a new meteorite is discovered that was previously unknown to science and is not associated with a known fireball or witnessed fall, it is described as a cold find. Making an entirely new discovery is one of the greatest achievements that a meteorite hunter can aspire to. Not only has the finder made an important contribution to the science of meteoritics, but his or her name will likely go down in the literature, in perpetuity, as the original discoverer.

Meteorites that have been on our planet for many years will, in most cases, have started to oxidize and, over time, may begin to look more and more like Earth rocks. Fusion crust decays or weathers away, and iron meteorites rust or acquire a patina that is often reminiscent of old bronze. In other words, old meteorites can be more difficult to spot than freshly-fallen ones because they are camouflaged.

If old meteorites are sometimes hard to spot, then I want to look for them in places where they will stand out. Hunting for cold finds in a heavily wooded forest, for example, or in zones that are rich in terrestrial rocks, or in areas with tall grass, will likely not be successful. Any meteorites that may have fallen there will be difficult to recognize among trees and boulders and will probably have been covered by falling leaves or decaying plants.

[left] Dry lake beds are often largely devoid of vegetation and can make for ideal meteorite hunting locations. [above] A new Nevada stone meteorite lying exactly where it was found. Note the relatively fresh black fusion crust, indicating a fairly recent fall.

Old meteorites will still appear darker in color than most Earth rocks, so if I want to locate them visually, I will search in areas where the odds are in my favor. Dry lake beds are a favorite search area for experienced meteorite hunters because they are wide open spaces, mostly devoid of vegetation, and generally have fewer terrestrial rocks than other environments. If you spot a dark-colored rock on the surface of a lake bed, it may have fallen out of the sky.

STRANDING SURFACES AND INCIDENCE OF FALLS

Numerous cold finds have been made in hot deserts in Northwest Africa, the American Southwest, the Australian Outback, and in Antarctica.

For the sake of argument, let us use a simplified model which suggests that a single meteorite, weighing 10 grams or more, falls on each square mile of the Earth every 10,000 years. In a region that experiences significant annual rainfall—northern Europe, for example—we would expect that meteorite to entirely decompose before the next statistically predicted fall 10,000 years in the future. In an arid environment, however, such as the deserts of Northwest Africa, the first meteorite would likely survive the 10,000-year period, so when a second meteorite falls on the same square mile 10,000 years later, we now have two potentially recoverable space rocks in a relatively small area. If we then extrapolate and look at a surface that has remained undisturbed for 100,000 years we could, theoretically, have ten recoverable meteorites per square mile.

Our theoretical model may be used to explain how over 30 different meteorites have been found in the San Juan strewnfield in Chile in an area of only a single square mile. The conditions in that part of the Atacama are ideal for the long-term preservation of meteorites, and the area is also very remote, so existing meteorites may not have been disturbed by wildlife, road building, farming, or other activities. There are few places in the world which are so perfect, but the find statistics at the San Juan site clearly demonstrate why we are particularly interested in old surfaces which are also dry and low in native vegetation. These areas where meteorites may have collected over great periods of time are sometimes known as stranding surfaces.

The Nullarbor Plain in Western Australia is another remarkable example of how old surfaces can produce abundant new meteorites. The Nullarbor is famous among meteorite enthusiasts as it encompasses the Mundrabilla iron meteorite strewnfield. Since its discovery in 1911, thousands of small irons have been found in the 30-mile long strewnfield, and they were all part of the same fall. A more intriguing statistic is that 600 different meteorites, unrelated to Mundrabilla, have also been found on the Nullarbor. Meteorite scientist Dr. Andy Tomkins joined my team on the Mundrabilla expedition and, while in the field, told me an amusing story about one of his meteorite hunting adventures in the Nullarbor. On the way to a potential site, he stopped his truck for a few minutes to have a look around. As he opened the

[left] Using an all-terrain vehicle (ATV) to scout a dry lake bed for meteorites. [above] How good are your eyes? I found this Mundrabilla iron meteorite on the surface where it had doubtless been lying for thousands of years. Its color is only slightly different from the surrounding soil. If you put in the time, and hunt in the right kind of environments, every now and then you will have the amazing experience of finding a meteorite sitting in the open air, waiting for you to walk by and pick it up. That can really make your day.

[top] Long-range scouting in off-road vehicles. Areas that may be good hunting sites can be explored by truck or ATV first. If a find is made, I GPS the location and spiral out from the find site on foot. [above] Multiple meteorites were found in this part of the Sahara while scouting by vehicle, so a more thorough search was then conducted on foot. The hunter is carrying a magnet cane, but no detector, because all meteorites found in the area were on the surface. [right] My team grids a field during a strewnfield hunt. Gridding refers to systematically covering an area using an organized search pattern.

door to his vehicle and got out, he almost stepped on a meteorite. After analysis in the lab, it was determined to be a completely new cold find.

Although Antarctica is covered in ice, it is still regarded as a desert due to its lack of rainfall. Conditions in Antarctica are unique. Unlike the Arctic, it is an actual geologic continent with mountains, valleys, and indigenous rocks. Meteorites have been falling on the continent for thousands of years and a great number have been found there. They become embedded in the ice and the dry, frozen environment preserves them well. Ice sheets travel, much like slow-moving rivers, so the imprisoned meteorites can be carried considerable distances. As ice rides up against Antarctic mountain ranges, wind causes it to erode, sometimes revealing meteorites. Although the circumstances of meteorite finds in Antarctica are unlike those in any other areas, the successful recovery expeditions there demonstrate just how many meteorites can fall in a finite area over long periods of time.

My friends Rob Matson and Sonny Clary have had great success making cold finds on dry lake beds in the United States. They have trained their eyes to look for out-of-place material in flat, desolate areas where very few Earth rocks occur. While Rob does most of his hunting on foot, Sonny prefers to cover large areas of ground quickly on an ATV. Carrying a magnet cane with you (see Chapter 13) is an excellent idea. It allows you to quickly and easily conduct a magnet test on any interesting-looking rocks.

If you find the right type of environment, spend sufficient time on the ground, and familiarize yourself with what weathered meteorites look like, there is a chance of making a new cold find for yourself.

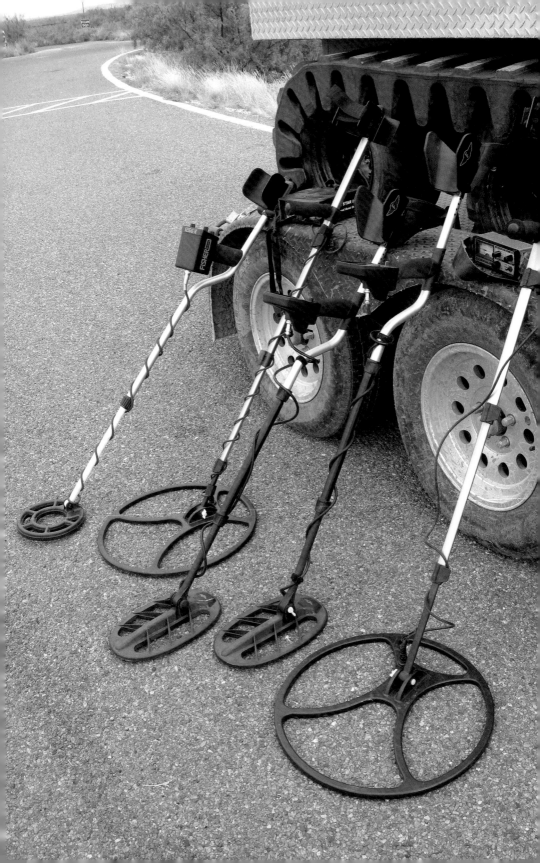

TOOLS OF THE TRADE

METAL DETECTORS

I have already explained in detail the critical fact that almost all meteorites contain a significant amount of ferrous (iron) material, typically about 20% in most stone meteorites, roughly 50% in stony-irons, and more than 90% in most irons. Meteorites that have been on Earth for some time may have become buried at varying depths, so a good metal detector becomes a crucial tool for the serious meteorite hunter.

While there are many different makes, models, and sizes, all metal detectors basically work on the same principle and most consist of the same primary components: control box, cable, coil (comprising a transmitter coil and shielded receiver coil), and frame. The control box sends an electromagnetic signal down the wire to the transmitter coil, which then sends that signal into the ground. When the electromagnetic field encounters a buried metallic object, a return signal is dispatched back to the receiver coil, then the control box, and is finally broadcast on a speaker, or through headphones to the user. A rigid plastic frame holds these components together, separates the metal circuits in the control box from the coil, and provides a handgrip for the user and space for batteries.

HAND-HELD DETECTORS (VLF)

The most widely-used detectors are hand-held units that employ VLF (very low frequency) technology. They are used for gold prospecting and relic hunting. They are lightweight, reasonably easy to use and, therefore, popular with hobbyists. If you have ever seen a retiree walking the beaches looking for lost watches or jewelry, he or she is almost certainly using a VLF detector. These hand-held models typically have a coil diameter of about 10 or 12 inches. They are used for locating shallow targets and most have a maximum depth of about 18 inches. VLF units are easy to transport, readily available from many different manufacturers, and relatively inexpensive. Their one drawback is limited range, which is a function of their small coils. VLF detectors can be used to hunt for any type of meteorite that contains iron, and are usually the best choice when hunting for stone meteorites, as their high degree of sensitivity can locate the small amounts of metal present in stones.

Not all metal detectors are created equal and some are simply better at finding meteorites than others. I am always trying out new equipment, new hunting techniques and new information sources. Years ago, online research took me to a thread on a Civil War forum. An older detector, the Fisher 1266, was taking a beating from one member after another. "I spent a whole hour digging down 15 inches to find a nail," one user protested. "Blast that

[above] Using my Fisher 1266 VLF detector to pinpoint a giant meteorite. The deeply-buried target was initially located using the "Big Rig," which has a range of at least 3 meters (9 ft). A test trench was excavated by the backhoe and, when we noticed rust appearing at the bottom of the dig, I jumped in with the 1266. Since the VLF detector, with its limited range, could now "see" the buried target, I knew we were very close to uncovering it. I have used this technique over and over again: A big PI coil locates a large target, then a smaller VLF detector is used to pinpoint it during excavation. [above right] Ten minutes later, we uncovered a giant meteorite. Note field magnet affixed to its surface, indicating high iron content.

detector!" another said. "It'll find any piece of rusty iron on the planet."
I was enthralled. The forum users were criticizing the 1266 for the very thing
I wanted in a detector. Relic hunters are looking for lead bullets, brass buckles,
and — if they're very lucky — maybe some stashed Confederate gold. They
don't want a detector that is excellent at finding decaying iron. But I do.
I purchased a used 1266 and found many meteorites with it. I liked it so
much, I decided to order a backup, but could not find another one. Much
later, I was told by a bomb disposal expert that the 1266 is particularly good
at finding land mines and all available machines had been snapped up by
buyers in Vietnam and Cambodia.

I used that detector on numerous television shows, including *The Best
Places to Find Cash & Treasures*, *Wired Science*, and the *Meteorite Men* pilot.
Later, a dial on the control box broke and I called Fisher. I was connected
to the repair department and told the gentleman I needed a 1266 repaired.
"We haven't supported that thing in years!" he laughed. When I explained
that this unit was special, and it helped me find a giant buried space rock
on *Meteorite Men*, he said: "Wait ... that was *you!?*" He was a fan of the
show and delighted to know someone was still using a 1266. Not only did
the repair department find a replacement part, but they also tuned the unit
and gave me a new coil. That was the start of my excellent professional
relationship with Fisher, and this tale demonstrates that useful hunting intel
can be sometimes found in unlikely places — like a Civil War forum. Relic
and nugget hunters are your allies. Joining a local detecting club may lead
not only to new friends, but also to new equipment tips and hunting tactics.

HAND-HELD DETECTORS (PI)

Pulse induction (PI) technology operates — in the broadest sense — in a similar way to VLF, but PI detectors are less susceptible to interference from mineralized ground, and can "see" through any type of layers: soil, sand, even underground shelves of rock. The electromagnetic field generated by any form of detector decays quickly as it travels down into the ground, and PI technology allows for the construction of larger coils. In simple terms, the larger your coil, the deeper it can "look" into the ground. The control box (which I sometimes call "the brain") of PI units can be connected to a variety of different coils. When hunting for iron or stony-iron meteorites which I suspect are buried at a moderate depth, I may use a larger 18-inch coil attached to a pulse induction control box, such as the Pulse Star II Pro.

PI detectors are ideal for sizable targets that are rich in iron, but most will receive no signal at all from a stone meteorite. The control box and battery pack on a typical PI detector are larger and heavier than a VLF unit, so I wear mine on a strap around my neck or in a backpack. An 18-inch coil has a maximum depth range of approximately 1 meter (3 ft). It is much heavier than a conventional VLF coil, so your effective hunting time will be limited when using one. Swinging an oversized coil for hours puts a significant strain on your arms and back, but also allows you to cover more ground.

[below] Can you have too much field gear? Probably not. The author in the Atacama Desert with one PI and one VLF detector [above right] The farther a detector's signal travels, the less area it covers and the diminishing "cone" of a VLF detector's electromagnetic field will miss deep targets. [lower right] The one-meter pulse induction coil is larger and heavier. It will cover more ground and has a much greater range, but it may miss smaller targets and can be more challenging to transport and operate.

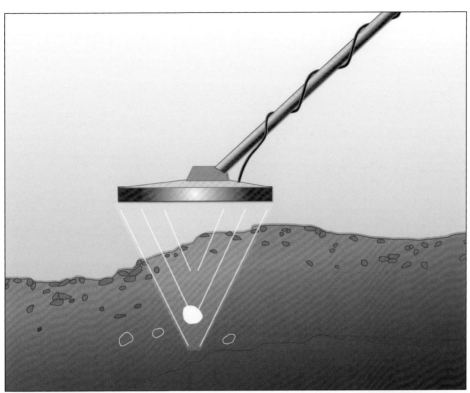

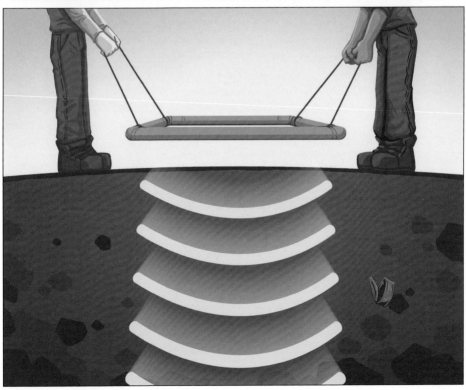

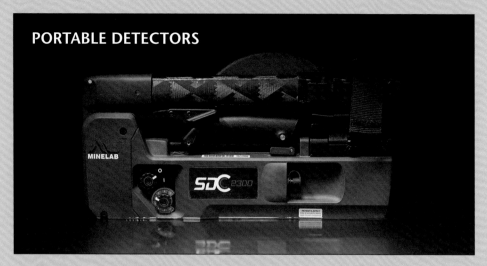

MINELAB SDC 2300 THE SASSY LITTLE DETECTOR WHO WANTED TO SEE THE WORLD

One of the problems routinely faced by meteorite hunters who use detectors is portability. It is one thing top stow a detector in your truck when driving to a hunt site in your home state. It is another if you are planning a trip to Siberia or the Australian Outback. Even when taken apart, most hand-held metal detectors will not fit in a standard suitcase, and a large duffel bag does not offer very good padding or protection for a delicate electromagnetic instrument. Enter the Minelab SDC 2300. Originally developed for the military as a seeker of unexploded ordnance, this ultra-sensitive unit miraculously folds down like a clever robot, into an eminently portable block that will easily fit in a suitcase or large backpack. The 2300 runs off standard D batteries, so power outlets and charging units are not required, meaning it can go anywhere with you. My 2300 has seen much of the world with me and has also found many meteorites. The 2300 is not a toy for the hobbyist. It is serious advanced tech designed for sensitivity and maneuverability. For the professional hunter on the move the 2300 is easily one of the best meteorite detectors out there.

GIANT DETECTORS (PI)

The "Big Rig" is a massive pulse induction (PI) detector designed by Steve Arnold. It has gone through many developmental stages over the years and consists of a giant coil mounted on a PVC sled and connected to a PI control box. We believe it may be the largest metal detector ever built.

As I have already discussed, the larger the coil, the greater its effective range, so the largest version of the "Big Rig" can locate a buried target of significant size at 3 meters (9 ft) or more, which is an extraordinary depth for any detector. The drawbacks in using a giant detector are the expense of building it and the difficulty in transporting the sled and coil. A working unit of that size costs in excess of $5,000 to construct and the act of towing it over rough ground often results in damage and additional repair costs. Building and operating a large unit is complicated and expensive, and requires a great deal of practice. It is not something recommended for the beginner, and should only be used in areas where the hunter expects to encounter large, deeply-buried targets that contain at least 50% iron.

When hunting the Muonionalusta strewnfield, north of the Arctic Circle in Sweden, my team was in a protected area where motor vehicles were prohibited. As the meteorites at that site are deeply buried, we still needed to use an extra-large detector. We used a pulse induction "brain" to power a portable coil that measured 2 meters (6 ft) on each side. It was large enough to find deep targets, yet maneuverable enough to use in a densely-wooded forest.

I designed the "Mule" Special Expedition Vehicle specifically for meteorite hunting. It has four-wheel drive, a high performance engine, special shocks, rock-crawling plates, and other custom features. Here, it tows the "Big Rig" metal detector across a meteorite fall site. The giant coil must be kept some distance behind, or it will detect the truck.

METAL DETECTOR TIPS AND TRICKS

Metal detectors do not use a great deal of power, and a set of fresh batteries will provide many hours of use with most units. As with any quality piece of electronic equipment, use good quality batteries, and do not mix different brands, or new and old batteries. It is a good idea to keep a spare set of fresh batteries in your backpack or equipment bag, and remove batteries from the detector if you will not be using it for extended periods.

TAKING CARE OF YOUR DETECTOR

Your detector is a powerful and sensitive piece of scientific equipment. Treat it as you would a good stereo, smart phone, or expensive camera. Try not to drop it or bang it into objects while searching. It is a good idea to invest in a carrying case if you will be transporting your detector in a vehicle or on an airplane. Most detector frames can easily be stripped down into smaller sections, and when I am going on an international hunt I break mine down and pack it carefully in a hard shell cargo case. Most detectors will work in the rain, but they might not like it very much. Try to keep your detector dry and do not submerge it in streams or lakes unless it is a waterproof model. Try to keep the control box clean and free from dust (not always an easy task in the desert) and do not leave it lying unattended in the hot sun for extended periods.

CARRYING SPARE EQUIPMENT

Professional meteorite hunters usually carry more than one detector, but that is not necessary for the beginner. Find a detector that you like and, if you plan on embarking upon extended trips, consider purchasing a second unit as a backup. There are many inexpensive but reliable used detectors on the market.

If I am traveling overseas, I always take at least two detectors, along with spare parts. When I visited the Imilac strewnfield in Chile's Atacama Desert, it took about four days of travel in each direction to get to the hunt site. I never want to take the chance of getting to a difficult-to-reach site only to discover that my detector has malfunctioned. Spares for modern detectors are not readily available and, even if they are, I do not want to waste valuable field time trying to repair damaged equipment.

REALLY GET TO KNOW YOUR GEAR

Much as a musician may search for years for the perfect guitar, you should find the detector that suits you best. Different detectors have different controls, varying operational parameters, and varying weights. I have found meteorites using equipment made by Minelab, Fisher, Teknetics, White's, Rutus, Pulse Star, and Lorenz. You may find a brand that you like better. The single most important consideration is that you purchase a detector that is sensitive to iron. Although this may seem obvious at first, be aware that most off-the-shelf detectors are designed with the hobbyist in mind and are intended to search for gold and other precious metals. Nearly all meteorites have significant iron content, but many or most modern detectors are built with a discrimination circuit that is used to filter out (discriminate) trash, such as iron, steel, and aluminum, when the user is looking for gold nuggets. If you use a detector in the incorrect mode, you definitely won't find any meteorites with it; so, when searching for space rocks, be very sure the discrimination setting is set to "off," or you will miss ferrous targets that could be meteorites. It is worth spending some time reading the manual, practicing, and getting to know your equipment before you take it out in the field. It is very frustrating to get to your hunting site and discover that you do not fully understand how your detector works.

METAL DETECTOR SCHOOL

This is a secret technique that I have never shared before. I live in the Sonoran Desert and the back section of my yard is wild, untamed wildernesss. It is just the sort of environment where you might find meteorites and that is quite handy for me. I know for a fact that there are meteorites in my yard because I put them there myself. Years ago. I buried those iron meteorites so

[above] This pyramid-shaped Glorieta Mountain meteorite reflected my detector's signal very well and produced a loud reading. The orientation of targets in the ground can affect how easy they are to find. A flattish object, parallel to the ground, presents a larger surface area and will usually register much more clearly to the detector than an object which is perpendicular to the ground.

long ago that I cannot remember exactly where they are, or how deep they are in the ground or — in fact — how many are still out there. That is why I call the wild part of my garden Metal Detector School. Every time I receive a new detector that I am excited to try out, I *really* try it out. Before it goes on an expedition, I take the new detector out to my favorite hunting ground, which is conveniently located about three minutes from my patio, and try to find meteorites. This is a reliable and realistic shakedown. If I can find targets in Metal Detector School, I should be able to find targets in a strewnfield, too. You can easily build your own testing range by burying nails, horseshoes, and so on. Or, if you are really serious, invest in a few inexpensive iron meteorites, bury them, and see if you can find them again. There is no substitute for learning by doing. And, as a bonus, your neighbors will almost certainly be very puzzled by your strange new behavior.

DIG EVERY TARGET

The experienced hunter can often tell — just by the sound emanating from the detector — whether or not a buried target is likely to be a meteorite. Attuning your ears to the variance in sounds produced by different targets might take months or years of practice, and even the professional hunter can easily be fooled. When I was hunting at the Henbury Craters site in Australia during 2010, my detector returned an extremely strong signal and I was convinced I had passed my coil over a tin can lying in high grass. I nearly walked away but, on second thought, dug the target anyway. It turned out to be a beautiful iron meteorite of nearly 500 grams, easily worth about $1,500 to $2,000. So, when you locate a good signal, be sure you find out what it is. Yes, you will dig up a lot of trash in the process, but you will learn, and will also not have to wonder, later, about unidentified targets left in the ground.

THE "RIGHT" DETECTOR IS ... FROM THE 1970s?

When I was hunting for pieces of the famous Pultusk, Poland fireball of 1868, I was frustrated because my modern, hi-tech American detector picked up every little scrap of iron in the trash-heavy strewnfield, which had been settled and farmed for centuries. It seemed I could not walk two feet without getting a target that sounded like a meteorite, but wasn't. To my amazement, my friend Marcin, who is a local hunter and expert on the Pultusk meteorite, produced a vintage Rutus Solaris detector made in Poland in the 1970s. I would consider this unit basic and low-tech by today's standards, but something about the simple, hand-made circuitry resonated with the stones that had been lying in wet ground for over 140 years. When passed over a Pultusk meteorite, the Rutus made a very particular sound that was noticeably different from the audio signature of man-made trash. I was so intrigued by this low-tech phenomenon that I asked Marcin to locate a used

[above] Some will turn their noses up at "obsolete" tech, but this vintage 1970s Rutus Solaris detector was unsurpassed at finding stone meteorites in its Polish homeland. Meteorite hunting has one thing in common with photography. Some photographers are purists who will not use anything but their favorite camera; others employ a variety of cameras and lenses depending on their needs. Some hunters swear by a single detector but, to me, the best detector is the one that does the job in the terrain I am working in (or "likes" a particular meteorite). Over time, you will discover the methodology that is right for you. Experiment with various detectors and compare notes with other detectorists. We learn best by doing.

model for me, which he did. I proudly added it to my detector collection, back home in the USA, as proof that sometimes an older and simpler piece of equipment is the best tool for the job.

PACK OUT TRASH AND FILL IN YOUR HOLES

My policy is to leave hunting sites cleaner than I found them. I always pack out my own trash as well as meteorwrongs. If I go to the trouble of digging up a horseshoe, a pile of nails, or a tin can, I put them in my backpack and dispose of them properly. It is also *extremely* important to fill in your dig holes. Some meteorite sites have been closed permanently because property was abused by irresponsible hunters. Cows and horses can stumble in a hole and break a leg, and such accidents do not make for happy ranchers. Respect the land and the landowner, close gates behind you, clean up after yourself, and you will be invited back to hunt another day.

MINIMIZE METAL ON YOUR PERSON

It is obvious that metal detectors find metal, but it is surprising how many detectorists overload themselves with metallic objects such as rock hammers, tools, steel canteens, and so on. A sensitive detector will pick up metallic objects on your body, so position your gear accordingly. Some detectors are so sensitive they will even register the tiny metal eyelets in your hiking boots, thereby giving a false signal. If your footwear contains metal—and most boots do—be sure to swing your detector away from your feet, and keep other metal objects as far away from the coil as possible.

HEADPHONES: YES OR NO?

Headphones do, in a sense, increase the hunter's ability to find deep targets, or targets that only contain a modest amount of iron. Wearing headphones allows you to hear fainter signals, get a better idea of the tone of the signal, and they minimize distracting outside noise. Using headphones can extend the battery life of your detector. As headphones may obscure exterior sounds, they can also be a potential hazard: You might not hear the warning of a rattlesnake, or may miss your hunting buddy calling for assistance. If you decide to hunt with headphones, keep the volume at a reasonable level and be extra vigilant for possible dangers.

PINPOINTERS: THE MINIATURE DETECTOR

Pinpointers are very small, hand-held detectors with a short range. As the name suggests, they are used to pinpoint a target that has already been discovered by a larger unit that has a greater range. It can sometimes be maddening trying to actually put your hands on a target that your primary detector has already "seen." Oxidation often causes meteorites and relics to take on the color of the soil they are buried in, so they may blend in

so well with their surroundings that you simply cannot see them unaided. I use powerful magnets to retrieve meteorites from dig piles, but magnets do not work on lead bullets, brass, gold, silver, and some other metals. Pinpointer technology has improved considerably in recent years and you may find them useful time-savers when sifting through piles of dirt, trying to locate an elusive target.

GLOBAL POSITIONING SYSTEM

Global Positioning System (GPS) units are devices that use a signal to communicate with orbiting satellites and then display the user's location in latitude and longitude. They are accurate to within a few feet and also typically show your compass heading and altitude above sea level. Seasoned meteorite hunter use GPS units to guide them to particular sites with known coordinates, mark the location of new finds, and record travel and distance covered. Many times I have made a find, logged it with GPS, then returned days or—in some cases—years later to continue the hunt. Documenting the location of each find is a useful record for the hunter, and find data are welcomed by meteoriticists who are attempting to plot all known meteorites from a particular find or fall. This is one of several ways in which hunters can actively contribute to meteorite science. At the end of the day, GPS will help you navigate directly back to your starting point and let you know how many miles your tired feet have covered.

[above] A GPS unit is used to log the location of a new meteorite find in Texas. GPS coordinates assist scientists with strewnfield data and can help you deduce where other meteorites may have fallen. [right] A 29-lb rare earth magnet demonstrates how well iron meteorites adhere to a strong magnetic source. [far right] A plastic trowel is used to excavate a pallasite. Metal digging tools could easily scratch or break delicate olivine crystals present on the meteorite's surface.

Modern GPS units are small and compact and easily fit in a vest pocket, backpack, or on your belt. More sophisticated models include color screens, topographical maps, and even satellite photos onto which the hunter or hiker can superimpose a route or hunting path. I never leave my truck without my GPS—in fact, I often carry two different models with me in the field—and I log the exact location of every find. A decent model can be purchased from camping stores or online retailers for about $100.

MAP AND COMPASS

While a GPS device is an invaluable tool, in my opinion nothing beats an old school map and compass. As a Royal Air Force cadet back in the United Kingdom, I studied advanced orienteering (map reading). As a visual person, I like to be able to see exactly where I am and where I am headed on a printed map. If my GPS gets lost, damaged, or—in rare cases—is unable to lock on to a satellite, a map and compass might end up being my only option for finding a safe route home, and you never have to replace the batteries in a map.

MAGNET CANES AND RARE EARTH MAGNETS

Since meteorites almost always contain iron, a good magnet is an essential item for your field kit. When I find a suspected meteorite on the surface, or when I excavate one from underground, the first thing I do is test it with a magnet. Most meteorites will jump to a powerful magnet and stick.

I use rare earth magnets on every expedition. They are lightweight, though somewhat fragile, and much more powerful than conventional

magnets. I generally use a 29-pound pull magnet, which is strong enough so that even an iron-poor meteorite will adhere to it. I have also constructed magnet rakes—devices that carry an array of magnets and which can be pulled by hand, or behind a vehicle. I have used magnets with an 80-pound pull, but they can be extremely dangerous and should be used with great care. I always wear gloves when handling them. A strong magnet can erase a computer hard drive, credit cards, hotel room keys, iPods, and similar devices, so be careful where you store them. I wrap my magnets in a woolen sock and transport them inside my hiking boots.

Magnets will also jump towards each other at blinding speed if placed too close together. If your finger gets between them when that happens, it is an unpleasant experience you will not forget.

When hunting for freshly-fallen meteorites on the surface, I test all interesting looking rocks with a magnet cane. A magnet cane is easy to construct for yourself. I have used walking sticks, metal poles, and even wooden dowel rods as a cane, and attached a magnet to one end using duct tape. Touching your magnet cane to possible meteorites can save you from bending over repeatedly to look at suspect rocks.

The Holbrook strewnfield in northern Arizona has produced thousands of pea-sized stone meteorites since the witnessed fall of 1912, and the Holbrook dunes are also home to a sizeable population of wild desert hares. Dried rabbit droppings can look remarkably like small chondrites, and one meteorite hunter who has been very successful at Holbrook is fond of saying: "If it doesn't stick to a magnet, don't pick it up!"

DIGGING TOOLS

When I head into the field, I throw a couple of good digging shovels into the back of my pickup truck. You never know when you might find a target that is out of reach for small hand tools. When I travel internationally, I carry a half-size shovel in my backpack. A folding military surplus entrenching tool is also a good option; it is lightweight and folds down for easy carrying.

The one indispensable tool for me is my rock hammer. I use a pickaxe-style tool with a steel blade and a durable plastic handle. I put one or two rare earth magnets on the flat surface of the blade, allowing me to both dig and test suspected meteorites with the same tool. A rock hammer can easily be carried in, or on, a backpack or belt mount. If you have a magnet affixed to your rock hammer, do not forget it is there. I have, more than once, leaned up against my truck, heard a loud *clunk!*, and discovered that my magnet and hammer had jumped out of their belt mount and securely affixed themselves to a vehicle door or side panel.

Another useful, but inexpensive, tool is a plastic gardening trowel, which weighs only a few ounces, costs a couple of dollars, and fits easily in a backpack. In my career, I have discovered numerous large pallasites. The surfaces of these rare and beautiful meteorites are often encrusted with clusters of fragile olivine (peridot) crystals. An accidental blow from a steel shovel could destroy or damage beautiful and delicate crystals that formed billions of years ago. So, after removing the top layer of soil and exposing part of a buried meteorite, we will often dispense with steel shovels and complete the final excavation with plastic trowels that are much less likely to damage a potentially valuable meteorite.

VEHICLES

Sometimes just getting to a site is half the battle. If you are going to be traveling on dirt tracks or exploring remote locations, be sure to select a suitable vehicle that can handle difficult terrain and which has plenty of ground clearance. I drive a modified 4WD pickup truck with top quality off-road tires and shocks. A valuable tip I learned from my late friend Jim Kriegh—discoverer of the Gold Basin strewnfield—is to always keep a spare car battery (fully charged), fan belt, and a professional tool kit with me in the vehicle. If you are working at an isolated location and discover that your truck has a dead battery, there may be nobody around to assist, and you could be facing a very long walk to get help or, in some cases simply be too far from civilization to safely hike out. And before heading out into the wilderness, check that your spare tire is inflated and in good shape.

Sometimes even the sturdiest 4WD truck is not sufficient to get where you want to be. When hunting at the Whitecourt Crater in Canada during the fall of 2009, the ground was covered with snow and even a powerful off-road truck could not navigate the narrow woodland tracks that led to the site, so my team rented ATVs to get us to the hunt location. I have also used ATVs to tow the "Big Rig" detector sled and to search by eye for recent falls. I have employed a wide variety of other transportation, including the Hydratrek amphibious tracked vehicle, the Orange County Choppers Meteorite Men Bike, and my custom off-road pickup known as the "Mule," to access challenging and out-of-the-way hunt sites.

Whichever vehicle you choose to work with, make sure it is in good running order before you set out and carry spare food and water at all times. When exploring Chile's Atacama Desert, my team was often so far away from civilization each truck had to carry several spare jerry cans filled with fuel. Gas stations were sometimes hundreds of miles apart, so we made sure every vehicle was well stocked with extra supplies. The serious meteorite hunter may travel to wild places, the likes of which most of humanity will never see.

Be certain you are well prepared. Your life may depend on it.

[left] Some of the colorful vehicles I have employed in my global search for space rocks. [below] This three-wheeled, off-road custom motorcycle was built for us by Orange County Choppers for use on my *Meteorite Men* television show.

EXCAVATING METEORITES
AND DOCUMENTING FINDS

A small meteorite buried a few inches below the surface may come out of the ground quickly and easily and become an instant addition to your collection. For shallow targets, I use my rock hammer, with magnet attached, and it is the perfect tool for the job.

Uncovering a large, buried meteorite is, for me, perhaps the most exciting part of my work. The process is reminiscent of an archaeological dig, but the treasure we are excavating is much older than the most ancient man-made artifacts. It can be an arduous and complicated procedure and may take several hours or more. As the soil, sand, or clay is removed, I always take a few minutes to photograph the emerging space rock. *In situ* photos are wonderful reminders of a new find and also important for expedition notes. Take your time and record the details. Remember that a buried meteorite may have started to fragment while encased in wet soil. Once the find has been removed from the ground, check the empty hole with your metal detector. In several cases I have found handfuls of small but attractive fragments at the bottom of a dig after a large meteorite has been pulled out. Such material should be placed in plastic specimen bags and labeled for future reference.

[left] This 69-pound iron meteorite discovered in the Swedish Arctic gave a strong signal on my detector, even though it was trapped under a glacial boulder that I estimated to weigh 300 pounds. [above] The same meteorite, photographed beside the Muonionalusta River, following recovery and a light cleaning.

I always carry extra specimen bags and a waterproof felt pen in my field bag or backpack, and write a field number, GPS location, or brief note on each bag that contains a meteorite. As time goes by it is easy to forget the details of a particular expedition. Spending a few seconds recording find numbers and locations in the moment will provide you with accurate data that you can refer back to at a later date.

Sometimes a meteorite is too deeply buried, the soil too dense, or the remaining time on site is too short to allow for a conventional excavation by hand. In those instances I might bring in a Bobcat or backhoe to speed up the process. I make arrangements with a local owner/operator, and even though a mechanized digger saves a great deal of time, I must be extra careful not to bash a buried meteorite with a quarter-ton steel excavator bucket. Finding a meteorite that is so big it requires the services of a tractor to retrieve it from the ground is a great problem to have, so if it happens to you, you will find a way.

When I was north of the Arctic Circle in Sweden at the Muonionalusta strewnfield, my team and I found a magnificent iron weighing 30.4 kg (67 lbs) at a depth of about 1.5 meters (3 ft) (see page 119). The meteorite had been transported by a long-vanished glacier and had been deposited in the terminal moraine—unsorted debris dropped as an ice sheet melts and recedes. The iron was securely wedged under a boulder that had also been dropped by the glacier. This find proved that my pulse induction detector could, indeed, see right though large rocks. It also proved that sometimes there is no substitute for hard manual labor. The hunting permit specified that mechanized vehicles were not allowed in the forest, so my four-person team had to dig the meteorite by hand. Our combined efforts were not sufficient to shift the boulder, which easily weighed several hundred pounds. Sometimes meteorite recovery is all about determination, and there was no way we were leaving that spectacular, large specimen in the ground. After several strategy discussions and many hours of experimentation, we greatly expanded the size of hole, dug around the boulder, and under it. We were eventually able to dislodge the trapped meteorite by having our friend and colleague Carin Österburg jump up and down on it until it worked loose. The boulder is still there.

Every expedition is different and every challenge requires a new solution. Persistence pays off and, once in a while, brute force wins out. This was nowhere better illustrated than at the beautiful Morasko Crater Preserve in Poland. My team was given special permission to hunt in this protected area and, using a sophisticated Lorenz Deepmax detector, acquired a strong signal on the second day. It then took three days of digging in the rain to remove the meteorite, weighing 34 kg (75 lbs), from under 2 meters (6 ft) of wet and viscous clay. Due to the protected nature of the site, we were unable to bring in a tractor and, weary from prolonged work, only managed to free the buried iron by press-ganging our tough Polish film crew into service.

[top left] After recording the location on a GPS unit, a fresh find from the Ash Creek fireball is bagged with cotton gloves to preserve the specimen. [above] Meteorite hunting sometimes feels like hard labor. It took two days to locate a large iron meteorite at the Morasko Crater Preserve, and another three days of challenging digging to free it from its wet and muddy tomb!

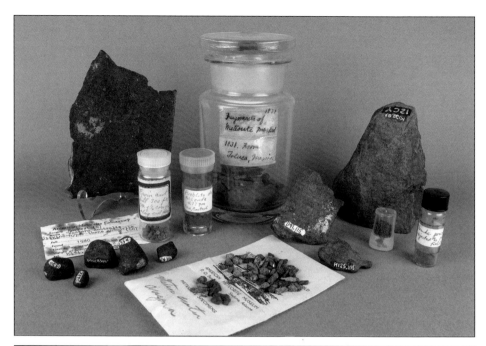

[top] Humanity's long experience with collecting and studying provides meteoritics with a rich history. Specimens from old collections sometimes come with hand-painted numbers or vintage labels, identifying their previous owners. [above] Examining a thin section under a microscope and with polarized light enables a specialist to determine a stone meteorite's composition. The specimen pictured is the CK4 carbonaceous chondrite NWA 4657. Photograph © John Kashuba.

AFTER THE FIND: NAMING AND CLASSIFICATION

An experienced meteorite professional can tell you whether or not your find is the real thing. I recommend carrying out a web search to see which companies currently offer such a service. A positive identification, however, is only the first step when it comes to a completely new meteorite.

A series of procedures must be followed in order to have a new meteorite formally recognized by the scientific community and that process can be fairly complicated. The first step is to have the meteorite classified. This requires a sophisticated laboratory analysis by a recognized meteoritics department and is typically not the sort of thing the average geology or astronomy department is equipped to carry out. The UCLA Department of Earth and Space Sciences, and the Center for Meteorite Studies at Arizona State University, are examples of the small number of accredited research institutions that can perform meteorite classifications.

If the new find is a stone meteorite, a thin section is made (see page 122). This involves removing a small piece from the specimen and grinding part of it down until it is so thin that light can pass through. The section is affixed to a glass slide and examined under a powerful microscope using polarized and normal light. Study under polarized light enables a specialist to determine which minerals are present. The majority of meteorite finds are ordinary chondrites. The classification process assigns them a letter such as H (high iron content), L (low iron content), or LL (low-low iron content). A number follows the letter and that indicates the amount of altering (by heat or water) that its chondrules experienced while still part of the parent body. Ordinary chondrites with a low number, 3.8 for example, have undergone very little alteration, while a number 6 denotes a high degree of alteration. So, an L4 chondrite such as Gold Basin will have a comparatively low iron content, along with chondrules that have undergone only a modest amount of deformation.

The classification of iron meteorites is dependent on a number of factors, including the ratio of iron to nickel and the size and structure of kamacite and taenite bands (nickel-iron alloys). Iron meteorite classification will typically involve removing a piece for grinding and etching, so its Widmanstätten pattern (see page 124) can be examined and measured. Non-destructive bombardment by an ion beam can determine the exact percentage of nickel and other elements. The presence of nickel is a key factor in verifying iron and stony-iron meteorites.

Laboratory time is expensive and in demand, so there is often a significant delay in getting a classification done, as many new meteorites are found each year, and there are only a few labs that have the experience and equipment to carry out this type of specialized work. In exchange for classification work, the

When polished and etched with nitric acid and alcohol, most iron meteorites display a lattice-like structure known as the Widmanstätten pattern. Intergrowth of the nickel-iron alloys kamacite and taenite creates this feature which is unique to meteorites. Note the difference in patterns between a prepared slice of Seymchan [above] from Russia and Gibeon [below right] from Namibia.

finder donates a minimum of 20 grams or 20% of the find (whichever is less), to the institution doing the work. The donated piece is referred to as the *type specimen* and will remain with the lab or university as part of their reference collection, enabling further study and comparison with future finds.

Once classification has been completed, details are presented to the Nomenclature Committee of the Meteoritical Society (NomCom), a group of meteoriticists who vote on proposed new names. A fall or find is typically named after the nearest town to the point of discovery. If the find was made in a remote area, the nearest geographical feature is sometimes used, making for colorful names such as Starvation Flat, Cat Mountain, Crab Orchard, Coyote Spring, and Camel Donga. In order to approve a new meteorite and give it an official name, the NomCom requires that the finder furnish them with the exact find location and the combined total weight of all known pieces. If a new find turns out to be an unusual or scientifically interesting meteorite, this process is sometimes fast tracked—as is the examination of new witnessed falls—but classification and naming of, for example, an ordinary chondrite may take years. After the NomCom has accepted a meteorite, the final step is to publish details in the *Meteoritical Bulletin*—an academic journal that lists all verified meteorites.

Although getting a new meteorite officially recognized can be a rather long and time-consuming process, I encourage you to go through the steps and follow proper procedure. New meteorite finds are important to science and, if you are the discoverer of one, your name will likely be included in the scientific literature of meteoritics for all time, and that is a significant accomplishment. Meteorites that have been properly named and classified are also worth more, in financial terms, to collectors. A recognized meteorite has pedigree and history and is usually more valuable than an unclassified one.

When a meteorite is found inside the boundaries of a known strewnfield, a specialist can usually carry out a simple visual comparison with other specimens that have already been recovered from the same site. If the new find shares common characteristics with other meteorites from that strewnfield, there is little point in getting an official classification done. For example: I will, from time to time, take a trip to the Holbrook strewnfield in northern Arizona. In 1912, a shower of thousands of stone meteorites rained down over the railroad town of Holbrook. There were many witnesses to the event and, to this day, small meteorites can still be found in the area if you are willing to put in the time. Most Holbrook meteorites are fusion-crusted individuals about the size and shape of a pea. So, if I am out walking the strewnfield with my magnet cane, and find a small, somewhat weathered stone meteorite that weighs a couple of grams and has the typical surface features of a Holbrook stone, I am not going to take up valuable lab time with a classification request. It is obvious to my trained eye that I have found a survivor from the 1912 fall. If, on the other hand, I am hunting in an area that does not encompass a known strewnfield and I discover a meteorite, it is likely new to science and I would turn over a portion of that find for study and classification. Every new find adds valuable information to the science of meteoritics.

PREPARING FOR AN EXPEDITION

The screenwriter Ed Podiam said: "There is no practical way to prepare for an epiphany or a catastrophe. You tell yourself you're ready, but then it happens regardless, for better or worse, and in ignorance of your best efforts." This insight applies particularly well to meteorite hunting because, no matter how carefully you prepare for an expedition, you can never fully and completely "expect the unexpected," even though the great science fiction writer, Douglas Adams, offered that as a key piece of advice to travelers in his masterpiece, *The Hitchhiker's Guide to the Galaxy*. Experienced adventurers prepare as best they can but must be ready to adapt, evolve, reboot, or revise the plan.

As you have learned from reading this book, most meteorites come to our little planet from the asteroid belt, by way of deep and cold space. Everywhere out there is on the way to nowhere. The average journey distance for a meteorite en route to Earth is 250,000,000 miles.

Every meteorite that reaches the surface of our home planet has overcome seemingly impossible, unmeasurable, and wholly cosmic odds to get here. When asteroids smash into each other—out there between Jupiter and Mars—blasting pieces in all directions, those shard-like fragments could, very literally, go anywhere: straight into another asteroid, off to frigid inter-solar-system blackness to be lost forever, or annihilated by the blinding heat and crushing gravity of our own sun. The few fragments that do, by chance, find their way to Earth encounter a moist atmosphere as fast as— well — a rocket, and our protective blanket of oxygen and nitrogen might cause them to skip, bounce, and hurtle back out into space. If they don't shear away, but instead, continue plowing towards Mother Earth through ever-thickening air, they may burn up completely, or explode into minuscule pieces as a result of a devastating and near-instantaneous temperature change. Or, most likely of all, they could just drop into the oceans that cover most of our planet, and sink to the seabed to be covered in silt as they rust into nothingness. Some land in sand dunes or Arctic snowfields, are swallowed by jungles, or— as in the case of one fireball I frantically investigated— have the very poor directional sense to make landfall in the middle of a top-secret military testing ground, never to be seen by human eyes.

Meteorites fall where they are going to fall. They pay no heed to the equator, or Earth's magnetic pole, or the government, or NASA, or anything other than the unflinching rules of physics and gravity. It is as simple as this: space, rock, atmosphere, boom!

There is no "special" section of Earth that gets a higher number of falls, and the odds are heavily against any meteorite making it here at all. The odds are also against you, or me, or anyone finding it. The successful meteorite hunter, therefore, must do everything possible to improve those odds.

If you intend to hunt in a place where meteorites have been found in the past, start by doing research. Do very thorough research. There was never a meteorite hunter who did too much research. On the other hand, most of us have glanced all-too-briefly at the existing conventional map of a new fall site and—eager to get out and get on with the hunt—thought to ourselves: "That area doesn't look so big, I'll sort it out when I get there." And then, when you do get there, you realize "that area" stretches, foreboding and featureless, in every direction until sunset, or—worse— is a mushy, swamp-sodden paradise for rattlesnakes and cottonmouths (this precise thing has happened to me). Perhaps, upon arrival, you realize the likely fall site is awash with densely-packed trees or corn stalks that would never consider allowing you to swing a detector among them, or maybe your favored ground is populated with red and white "NO TRESPASSING" signs (in New Mexico, while hunting the Glorieta Mountain strewnfield, I once saw such a sign that stated: "SURVIVORS WILL BE PROSECUTED.") Whenever possible, know where you are going before you get there, and pack accordingly. If you are going to the Arctic (as I have, repeatedly), you may need snow gear. If you are going deep into the poison-ivy rich swamps of Alabama in the summer (as I have, fortunately only once), waders and snake gaiters will be far more useful.

If a meteorite was found at the site you are headed to, try and determine precisely where and under what circumstances the discovery was made. Begin your search there and work outwards. Meteorites often fall in clusters, so there may be others nearby. Was the initial find deeply buried and discovered with the help of a detector, or was it lying on the surface? The age of the fall and the type of meteorite will dictate your search methods.

Take everything you need, but try to make sure you need everything you take. This is tricky for me because I like to have every conceivable bit of gear I might want, but I also like to travel light. Those two concepts do not mix well together, so I have to play Give and Take as I prepare for each expedition. Many of the things I pack in (energy bars, soluble vitamins, trail mix, etc.), will not need to be packed out with me because they are consumed during the expedition, hopefully making room in my bags for finds and souvenirs.

Wondering what to do with those old sneakers and socks that are nearly worn out? They make excellent expedition fodder. Wear them around camp, or on travel days, and trash them on your final day. If you are operating in an underprivileged country, you may well find a grateful soul who will enthusiastically give a good forever home to the used boots, cooking pan, or old sleeping bag that you cannot be bothered to take home. That way, if you fall in love with a camel blanket or a fez, you will have room in your bag to bring them back as mementos, or as gifts for your significant other. Or your pet (my cat reclines daily on blankets I have brought back for her from

Lapland, Australia, and my favorite market in Marrakech).

The only thing better than traveling light is discovering, when you really need it, that you *did* bring the spare battery pack. Learning what to take, and how much of it, are acquired skills.

To help you, here is a concise recap of some of the information provided earlier in the book, along with a list of indispensable items the serious hunter will almost always need, and some tips and tricks learned the hard way from a lifetime of travel amounting to well over a million miles by land, sea, and air.

GOOD HIKING BOOTS

You only get two feet and they are going to carry you everywhere you need to go on the way to making your first, or next, meteorite find. My friend Mike Miller, a highly successful and determined meteorite hunter, once stated the obvious when we were in the field: "You have to walk over a meteorite before you can find it." But then, sometimes obvious advice is the best advice.

Take care of your feet so they can walk over that meteorite for you. Put them inside good, sturdy, lightweight, comfy hiking boots. The comfy part is very important. If your feet are not happy, they will definitely not do a good job of porting you around the strewnfield for eight or sixteen hours a day (depending on your level of gusto). For the serious hunter, sneakers will not cut it during the long haul, especially in rough terrain. Socks are important, too. On long or arduous hunts and hikes, I wear thin liner socks underneath larger cotton socks. The liners wick away moisture, help prevent blisters, and provide extra cushioning.

DAY PACK OR UTILITY BELT

Choose a lightweight day pack when doing actual hunting and always take it with you. Even on a short hike. If you make a find, or get lost, or both, a "short walk" can very quickly turn into the long hike you were not prepared for. Only put essentials in your day pack. Leave your flip flops and your bedtime reading in the tent or vehicle. Some of us have been hefting packs in and out of craters and up and down mountain ranges for decades. As a result, some people's backs may have started complaining about the abuse. Osprey makes a terrific utility belt that comes with a one-liter water bottle in each of two side pockets, along with plenty of zippered pockets for other necessities. Tired back? Let your hips take the brunt for a change.

WHICH METAL DETECTOR SHOULD I USE?

If you are looking for buried meteorites you will need a good quality metal detector. A cheap kids' model from your local megamart is simply not going to do the job, and will not "see" the rare and valuable space rocks you are searching for. Different detectors are better at finding different types of meteorites. Do your research or ask me. My company, Aerolite Meteorites, Inc., is an authorized Minelab and Fisher metal detector dealer with decades of meteorite-hunting expertise and will be glad to advise you on which detector we think is right for you.

MAGNET CANES

I take magnet canes into the field for a reason. As you now know, almost all meteorites contain iron and will stick well to a magnet. There are, however, a whole lot of other rocks out there that look like meteorites, but aren't. Using a magnet cane prevents you from having to bend over and pick up rocks one thousand times a day. If that doesn't sound like such a big deal, try picking up a thousand rocks in one day — in the heat, or on a mountainside, perhaps while being irritated by mosquitos, flies, or cactus spines — only to discover that none of them are meteorites.

GPS

When searching in known strewnfields, I log every find. That helps me understand the fall pattern of meteorites and may give me clues about the locations of other, undiscovered pieces. GPS data can be very useful to meteorite researchers who are building strewnfield maps, and a GPS unit can also save your life. Eager to start a desert hunt, I once took off in such a hurry that I lost my bearings and it was well after sunset before I found my way back to the truck, with great relief, and a promise to myself that I would never do that again. It is very easy, especially in tundra or flat desert, to lose site of where you parked. GPS the location of your vehicle or campsite *before* you head out to hunt, so you can find your way home later when you are tired and it is getting dark.

WATER AND NOURISHMENT

Most of us know that we are supposed to drink about two liters of water per day, and that is under normal conditions. If you are hiking around, up and down ravines, swinging a detector, carrying tools and pack, and digging in the dirt, your body needs a lot more water than in "normal conditions." Carry extra water in the field with you at all times. Use a backpack canteen or multiple water bottles. I never leave the truck or campsite with less than 1.5 liters on my person.

The excitement and exertion of meteorite hunting burns calories. Take energy bars or trail mix in your day pack with you. When you get hungry, miles from base camp, you will be glad you have them. Eat some real food for breakfast and dinner. You need energy in the field, so find a way to mix in fresh fruit, greens, and protein when you can. Crackers and sandwiches are not sufficient fuel for the successful adventurer. I pack two energy bars, one powdered vitamin pack, and one electrolyte pack for each day I expect to spend in the field. Pour the vitamins and electrolytes into your water bottle. They taste good and ensure you get your minerals and vitamins.

FIRST AID AND SAFETY

I always keep a quality folding camping knife on my belt and carry a small first aid kit with me if I am hunting alone or far from camp. More robust first aid kits are stowed in the field vehicles or tents. My friends who have skin cancer now wish they had used more sunscreen when they were younger. Wearing a decent, wide-brimmed hat helps prevent excessive sun exposure, and hopefully sunstroke, and also makes you look a bit like Indiana Jones, which is never a bad thing. If it appears that weather conditions may change during your field days, put a small poncho or emergency blanket in your pack. Camping gear is very hi-tech these days and you can easily find examples of each that only weigh a few ounces.

In some instances, such as traveling in the Atacama Desert or the Australian Outback, my team took trained medics and / or survival guides with us, because we were so very far from civilization that an emergency evac — even by helicopter or flying doctor — was not an option. It was money well spent. Hazards vary by country and season and it is extremely valuable to have a local expert on board to point out what is dangerous and what isn't. They also usually have great campfire stories.

INSECTS

Some insects are annoying; others are deadly. I never wear open-toed shoes in the field, and I rarely wear shorts because both increase your exposure to bites and stings, as well as the sun. Keep a small bottle of insect repellent in your pack and you should have antiseptic wipes in your first aid kit. I also carry a folded mosquito / fly net that is not much bigger than a wine cork. It fits into a tiny pocket on my belt pack. If you are assaulted by swarms of mosquitos or biting flies, as I have, you will be very glad you have that net.

INSURANCE AND EVACS

If you are going to get serious about meteorite hunting, you may find that your final destination is way out there in the strange and hostile world. If that is the case, you may consider investing in a premium insurance service. Companies like Global Rescue offer medical and military evacs, should you find yourself in a really dicey situation. In remote areas, you are simply not going to get conventional cell phone service, so I recommend a sat phone for major expeditions. They are somewhat pricey to rent and to use ($2 per minute is typical, plus rental fee for the unit), but that $2 call could save your life, or the life of a team member.

PACKING

Most airlines charge for each checked bag and the typical weight limit is about 23 kg (50 lbs) per bag. Put heavy and valuable items like cameras and laptops in your carry-on, as most airlines don't weigh them, and you do not want that stuff thrown around by baggage handlers anyway. I travel with a small, portable hand scale that tells me how much my bags weigh. It is very handy to know that before you get to the airport. On a major expedition I travel with matching heavy-duty rolling bags. I split up the big stuff: my folded-down Minelab SDC 2300 detector loves to travel and it goes happily in one bag; my hiking boots, rock hammer, and magnet cane go in the other.

We all need clothes, so wrap your detector in a field jacket or jeans for added protection. If you are driving to the hunt site, your detectors still need to be treated with care and respect. Expert meteorite hunter Twink Monrad is also a seamstress and made snappy cloth detector bags for herself and her hunting partner, the late Jim Kriegh.

Meteorite hunters are never without rare earth magnets, and those magnets will happily wipe your credit card, hotel card key, or iPod, so I bundle one in a wool sock and put it in a hiking boot. When driving, magnets love to travel clamped to the bed of your truck until you need them.

MEMORIES AND THE EXPERIENCE

Meteorite hunting is not all about the finds. It is also about the journeys we embark upon and the friends we go with, or make along the way. Take a small camera or smart phone with you. Later, you will look back at your adventure photos with delight. Don't forget to pause for a moment and take an *in situ* photo of your finds. Your friends will be impressed when you get home and they will exclaim: "You found *that!?*" You might take a little notebook and keep a daily trip journal. I always carry a thick paperback book with me, because you never know when you might have to occupy an hour, or a day, while a tire is being changed or an airplane refueled.

Above all, remember that no matter how much you plan, nothing ever turns out quite the way you expected. Be nimble, like the snake who glides between boulders. Be ready to adapt to changing situations and try to appreciate the opportunities you have been given. Meteorite hunting is not for everyone, but every hunt is an adventure.

The greatest meteorite hunters know that every good find happens because of a combination of research, skill, knowledge, determination, and chance. Working in film and television for over a decade, I have learned that the best adventures are always the unscripted ones, and in his memoir, *Travels with Charley,* John Steinbeck observed: "We find after years of struggle that we do not take a trip; a trip takes us."

May you be taken by a good one.

IN THE FIELD: FUN AND SAFETY

Although meteorites have always been the great interest of my life, there was no particular day when I woke up and said: "I am now going to be a professional meteorite hunter." Recovering, collecting, and studying meteorites began for me as a hobby, grew into a passion, and ultimately became my profession.

Hunting for meteorites is not the best way to make a living; it is a calling. You are not likely to head out into the field and strike it rich on the first day, or in the first year. Meteorites are rare, and finding them requires patience, skill, dedication, knowledge and a lot of hard work. You might hunt in a strewnfield for an entire week and find one walnut-sized space rock that is only worth $50—or you may find nothing at all. Financially, meteorite hunting does not often provide a good return on the investment of time, equipment, and expenses. But if, like me, you can appreciate the wonder, delight, and excitement that comes from being the first person—ever, in the history of the world—to see and hold a particular visitor from space, then meteorite hunting may be the right adventure or profession for you. If, on the other hand, your aim in life is a comfortable existence with a big house and expensive cars, then you may do better embarking upon a different career path. Although I do make my living from meteorites, it is the joy and the thrill of finding them that keep me going.

Meteorite hunting is time consuming and can be strenuous, even dangerous. Much of my work revolves around desert hunting. Deserts are, obviously, very dry and conditions often allow meteorites to be preserved for centuries or even longer. Some deserts are also home to snakes, scorpions, poisonous spiders, abandoned mine shafts, unexploded bombs, and other hazards. For safety reasons, I usually prefer to have someone out there with me. If you encounter dangerous wild animals, there is strength in numbers, and I have friends who, while hunting alone, broke a leg or suffered other serious, life-threatening injuries and had to literally drag themselves back to safety.

Some meteorite hunters enjoy the social aspect of expeditions and adventuring together in large groups. I prefer to work as part of a small, trusted, and experienced team. Others, like the great meteorite hunter Sonny Clary, are loners who head deep into the wilderness by themselves or with their dog. Meteorite hunting is, for me, largely a solitary and contemplative occupation. Steve Arnold and I have been working together for over twenty years and have embarked upon scores of expeditions. We look out for each other, pitch in to move heavy gear, share ideas and strategies, but—despite all of that—when our boots hit the ground we automatically take off in different directions and follow our own Muse.

Walking alone across a startling desert landscape gives me time to think, to enjoy the stillness, and to ponder the remarkable origin and history of the space rocks for which I am searching. Many times, for no good reason, an inner voice has said to me: "Geoff, go look over *there*," or, "The meteorites are just on the other side of *that* mesa!" I am a scientist and I do not really believe that such hunches or whims can empirically lead to anything, but I follow them anyway.

Although I enjoy solitude to a degree, when the hunting day is done, and I return to the truck—exuberant because I have made a great discovery, or disappointed because my specimen bags are empty—it is good to know that my hunting buddy is somewhere nearby and has my back.

That is how I do it, but that is not how you have to do it. This book is the world's first-ever guide to meteorite hunting. I learned by doing, and so will you. Be careful, be smart, keep your eyes open, and please let me know when you find your first space rock. That will definitely make my day.

Good hunting!

POSTSCRIPT
GO METEORITE HUNTING WITH ME

When I was starting out in the meteorite world, I had the good fortune to dine with Marlin Cilz of the Montana Meteorite Lab—a respected expert and preparation artist. I was very concerned because one of my iron meteorites was showing a little bit of rust. I asked him what to do about that. He laughed and told me not to worry about it because iron is resilient and we are only caretakers of the meteorites we find and collect. They will still be here long after we are gone.

Meteorites have survived an incredible journey of literally astronomical proportions and some carry within them clues to the answers of the great questions in science: How old is the universe? How did it form? What are the origins of life on our planet and is there other life, out there— somewhere? As such, meteorites deserve to be treated with care, perhaps even reverence. They are not a simple commodity like gold, diamonds, or copper. Part of being a responsible hunter and collector is acknowledging that a portion of important new finds should always be made available to academia for study; meteorites should be properly cared for, documented, labeled, and curated; and plans should be made for what will become of them after their human caretakers have passed on.

After all, they did travel a very long way to get here.

I got my first metal detector when I was a kid in the early 1970s. It was a simple affair with one on/off switch, an output for a single mono earpiece, and nothing else. I learned the ropes hunting for relics in the smelly quagmire of London's River Thames at low tide, and on disused Royal Air Force fighter bases in southern England. We've come a very long way since then. Today's professional detectors are sophisticated, complex treasure-finding machines. And meteorites can be extremely difficult not just to find, but also to identify in the field. Despite that, many want to find their own, so I personally teach small groups of people how to do it — hands-on and no-nonsense — in the USA and around the world. I take teams to specially-constructed strewnfields (where we have buried meteorites) to show them the basics, and then on real hunts to real strewnfields. The results have been astounding. Hundreds of meteorites found by scores of adventurers, of all ages, who now take that earned expertise with them wherever they go.

As I have said in this book, the best way to learn is by doing. And we *teach* by doing. We provide everything: locations, detectors, equipment, vehicles, accommodation, and meals. And, most importantly, unparalleled expertise.

Join the adventure at **www.meteoriteadventures.com**

ADDITIONAL RESOURCES

AEROLITE METEORITES INC

Aerolite Meteorites is a world leader in meteorite recovery, sales, and education. We have supplied meteorites to most of the world's major museums and universities as well as collectors of all levels. We are also authorized Minelab and Fisher metal detector dealers: **www.aerolite.org**

AEROLITE EUROPE

Our UK-based offices cater specifically to customers in Europe and our European director, Nick Howes, is an admired educator, and meteorite, astronomy, and spaceflight expert: **www.meteorites.io**

METEORITE ADVENTURES

I lead small groups on actual meteorite hunting adventures and teach them how to do what I do. Learn more: **www.meteoriteadventures.com**

METEORITE MEN

The adventure television series, *Meteorite Men* for Discovery networks won two Telly Awards, aired all over the world, has been seen by tens of millions of people, and popularized meteorite hunting and collecting. Official site: **www.meteoritemen.com**

METEORITE MINUTE

Meteorite Minute is an educational short film series produced by Desert Owl Productions and directed by Christian Meza. Episodes are available, free of charge on YouTube: **www.youtube.com/geoffnotkin**

METEORITE TIMES

A free monthly online magazine presenting the best in meteorite news, research, and reports, *Meteorite Times* features exclusive columns by noted meteorite professionals: **www.meteorite-times.com**

NATIONAL SPACE SOCIETY

I am on the Board of Governors of the National Space Society (NSS), and science columnist for their magazine, *Ad Astra*. The NSS is the world's largest and oldest grassroots international spaceflight organization, and is dedicated to promoting the human exploration of space: **www.nss.org**

THE AUTHOR

I invite readers to connect with me on social media, via Twitter, Instagram, YouTube, and Facebook: **@geoffnotkin**

ACKNOWLEDGMENTS

Beth Carrillo started with me in 2010 as a junior sales assistant, answering the phones, emails, and—as she likes to claim—allegedly emptying the cat's litter box, although I don't actually recall that. Beth worked her way up the ranks at Aerolite Meteorites, Inc., and is now company president as well as an accomplished television producer and businesswoman. Her fierce devotion to the company has allowed me to travel, adventure, and write this book. She has also been the most admirable of friends and colleagues.

I met Christian Meza late on a Sunday night in the lobby of the Toronto Hyatt at the International Space Development Conference. He was giving a virtual reality demo to future astronauts, so I offered him a job on the spot. It was one of the better business decisions I've made. He is now Chief Technical Officer at Aerolite Meteorites and took some of the most striking photographs in this book.

My Executive Assistant, Melissa Silva, is the book's Managing Editor and an officer at Stanegate Press. Her contributions to the project are excellent and numerous. Aerolite's Sales Manager, Marissa Quintana, helped keep the business running so I could off-road it through some of the world's wildest places. Antonia Andros provided the beautiful, original technical illustrations.

The Fallen Sky: An Intimate History of Shooting Stars is one of the finest books about meteorites ever published. Its author, Christopher Cokinos, wrote the introduction for me. There is an old rock 'n' roll adage that it is a bold, yet risky, idea to have a band better than your own perform as your opening act. A gamble of that sort makes the headliner work harder to try and keep up. Such is the case when an author of Christopher's stature introduces my book. I am grateful for his friendship and support and the way in which he has used his beautiful prose to illuminate and explain the wonders of meteorites.

Dr. Joel Schiff and Dr. Larry and Nancy Lebofsky worked closely with me over the years and became respected friends. They gave me the opportunity to see many of my works in print in *Meteorite* magazine during their admirable careers with that publication. Nancy and Larry brought their expertise to bear and served as the editors for this book. I thank them for helping making *How to Find Treasure from Space* the best that it could be.

Paul Harris and Jim Tobin of Meteorite.com, The Meteorite Exchange, and the online magazine *Meteorite Times* are cornerstones of the world of space rocks. Paul and Jim have supported me and my work, and have helped to build and educate the community in so many ways, for so many years, that I simply could not compile a list of everything they have accomplished.

Dr. Hobart King, the publisher of Geology.com—one of the world's top science websites—invited me, many years ago, to write a series of articles for him, which became the *Meteorwritings* column. Dr. King generously allowed me to reproduce some of that material in this book.

Rob Matson is one of the most brilliant people I have ever met. His original work with strewnfield research, lake bed hunting, and Doppler radar is both groundbreaking and influential. Time and again, Rob has assisted me with technical advice, local intelligence, and strewnfield data. When I grow up, if I am half as smart as Rob, I shall consider myself a genius.

Sonya Bourn, Senior Producer for *Meteorite Men*, not only steered three seasons of our adventure television show through 120,000 miles of travel and untold hazards and difficulties, but also became a friend, colleague, and ongoing supporter of my work. Executive Producer Ruth Rivin first came up with the idea for *Meteorite Men*, and also became a valued friend, as did Kathy Williamson and Bob Melisso who, between them, directed the early episodes of our show with great style and dedication.

Sonny Clary ("I know they're out there Geoff. They just *gotta* be!") appeared in two episodes of *Meteorite Men*, provided a roof over my head, shared his ATVs, his knowledge and experience, and is the finest of expedition companions. As a fireman and EMT, he has dedicated his life to saving and serving others. In his spare time he takes off into the wilds with his dog, Brix, and is a courageous and successful meteorite hunter.

I have shared grand adventures with Ruben Garcia, a fellow musician and accomplished hunter. Ruben guest-starred in the "Ash Creek Fireball" episode of *Meteorite Men.* He is a meteorite expert and a man of integrity and character. I have benefited greatly from his friendship and expertise. The same is true of Mike Miller, a generous, inventive, and determined meteorite hunter, with whom I have enjoyed many an adventure.

Terry Boudreaux once initiated a conversation about a television show. Thank you for lighting a small fire that turned into a big one.

Many luminaries in meteoritics, astronomy, paleontology, and spaceflight have provided friendship, support, or encouragement along the way. They include my good friend Nick Howes, Director of Aerolite Europe; Mike Jensen of Jensen Meteorites and his brother Bill; the late Dr. Art Ehlmann and Teresa Moss of the Oscar E. Monnig Meteorite Collection; Drs. Laurence Garvie, Carleton Moore, and Meenakshi Wadhwa of the Center for Meteorite Studies at ASU Tempe; Dr. Carl Agee of the Institute of Meteoritics at UNM; Dr. Chris Herd of the University of Alberta, Edmonton; Professor Dante Lauretta of OSIRIS-REx; Dr. Jane MacArthur; Dr. Randy Korotev; author and adventurer Professor Roy Gallant; my great pal Geoff Cintron, formerly of Island Meteorite; Matt Morgan of Mile High Meteorites; fellow hunter and neighbor Twink Monrad; David Eicher and Michael Bakich of *Astronomy* magazine; my resourceful and sleuth-like researcher Katherine Rambo; genius inventor Bill Mason of Paleobond; my fine gem show partners John and Tracie Bennitt of Dinosaur Brokers; Andrzej Pilski, publisher of *Meteoryt* (Poland); Dr. Alain Carion, whose published works and research have been an inspiration to me; Hank Ebes and Tom Kapitany of the National Dinosaur Museum, Canberra; George Winters of the AAPS; Rick Tumlinson; authors Rod Pyle and Howard Bloom, and all at the National Space Society; and science writer and meteorite enthusiast extraordinaire, Dr. Phil Plait.

Special thanks to Blaine and Blake Reed; IMCA president Bob Falls and his wife Carol; Qynne Arnold; Aubrey Rose Vaughn; Eric Schumacher and Ginger Ferguson; Bob Cucchiara; Michael Blood and Angel Hayes; Bob Holmes; José Guggiari; Martin Altmann; Jeff Kuyken; Maria Haas; Mike Martinez; Art Jones; Martin Horejsi; Derek Yoost; Bill and Denise Kroth; Thomas Österburg of the mysterious One-Ton Club, and his daughter Carin; Dr. Andy Tomkins; the late O. Richard Norton, Dorothy Norton and John Kashuba; Nate Ditto; Eduardo Jawerbaum; Hans Koser; Rob Wesel, Mike Bandli, and Jason Philips; Brad Kern; Rob Reisner; Marlin Cilz; Leigh Anne DelRay-Crowell; Paul and Wendy Swartz; Amy Shira Teitel, fellow science writer and host of *Vintage Space*; artist Jessica Milligan Stone, who made the treasure chest pictured on the cover; Lisa Marie Morrison and Pablo Rivera; and my much-missed friend and mentor, the late Professor Jim Kriegh.

Al Mitterling once sat with me at a Mexican restaurant in Tucson and encouraged me to write a book about meteorites. That conversation grew into this work (and also *Rock Star: Adventures of a Meteorite Man*).

Guy Rovella of Aardvark Printing brought this book into the tangible world and Norma Morrison assisted with copy editing.

Becca Gladden has been my publicist and public relations director for many years. She has assisted with a myriad of projects, with her customary good humor and exceptional attention to detail, not least of which was proofreading this very book.

My friend, expedition partner, and fellow *Meteorite Men* television host, Steve Arnold, is one of the greatest meteorite hunters in all of history. He helped show me the ropes when I was starting out. We have shared adventures too numerous to count, over hundreds of thousands of miles, during the past few decades and Steve took many of the photos in this book. *How to Find Treasure from Space* would likely not exist without him.

Allan and Iris Lang of R. A. Langheinrich Meteorites and the Langheinrich Fossil Preserve have been admired friends and colleagues for many years. Al is a major figure in meteoritics and paleontology and his innovative, generous, and ongoing contributions to science, commerce, collecting, and my personal journey have been enormous.

This book is dedicated to him.

ABOUT THE AUTHOR

Meteorite specialist Geoffrey Notkin starred in three seasons of the hit, multi-award-winning television adventure series *Meteorite Men* for Discovery networks, and two seasons of *STEM Journals*, for which he won two Emmy Awards. Notkin has also appeared in shows for Nat Geo, History Channel, Travel Channel, TLC, PBS, A&E, NASA, and the BBC. He is a science writer, TEDx speaker, and an Edinburgh Fringe Festival performer. He has appeared on *Coast to Coast AM*, *Fox News*, *Varney & Co*, and the *Today* show, and has been interviewed by The BBC World Service, *The Washington Post*, *Huffington Post*, Reuters, Associated Press, *Universe Today*, and numerous other media outlets.

Notkin has published hundreds of articles on science, history, travel, and the arts, with his work appearing in *National Geographic*, *Smithsonian*, *The Guardian*, *The New York Times*, *Astronomy*, *Astronomy Now*, *Sky & Telescope*, *USA Today*, *Wired*, *Reader's Digest*, *Robb Report*, *The Village Voice*, and many other publications. He is the author of several books, including *Rock Star: Adventures of a Meteorite Man* and *My Incredibly Strange and Amazing Real-Life Adventures in the World of Comic Books*. His spaceflight and tech column, "Throwing Pebbles at the Sky," is exclusive to the National Space Society's print magazine, *Ad Astra*.

Notkin is founder and Chief Executive Officer of Aerolite Meteorites, Inc. (www.aerolite.org), a leader in meteorite research, recovery, and education and he has worked with, and provided specimens to, most of the world's major institutions including the American Museum of Natural History, New York; the Natural History Museum, London; the Natural History Museum Vienna, Austria; the Center for Meteorite Studies at ASU, Tempe; the Institute of Meteoritics at UNM, Albuquerque; and the Oscar E. Monnig Meteorite Collection in Fort Worth. He is a member of the celebrated Explorers Club, the Association of Applied Paleontological Sciences (AAPS), and the International Meteorite Collectors Association (IMCA).

An accomplished film producer, Notkin's credits include the documentaries *Neil Gaiman: Dream Dangerously* and *First to the Moon: The Story of Apollo 8*, and the features *Revenge of Zoe,* and Philip K. Dick's *Radio Free Albemuth.*

He sits on the Board of Governors of the National Space Society; the Board of Directors of the Astrosociology Research Institute; the Board of Directors of the Science, Arts, and Space Institute; and the Advisory Board of Deep Space Industries.

The minor planet 132904, discovered at Mount Palomar, was named "Notkin" in recognition of his contributions to science, education, and the arts.

Notkin was born on 14th Street in New York City and grew up in London, England. He studied geology, astronomy, photography, writing, and design in London, Boston, and New York, and now resides in the Sonoran Desert of southern Arizona, with one eccentric cat, no wives, and no children.

Connect with him on social media via **@geoffnotkin**